Mutant Materials in Contemporary Design

Paola Antonelli

Mutant Materials in

Contemporary Design

The Museum of Modern Art, New York

Distributed by Harry N. Abrams, Inc., New York

Published on the occasion of the exhibition *Mutant Materials in Contemporary Design*, organized by Paola Antonelli, Associate Curator, Department of Architecture and Design, The Museum of Modern Art, New York, May 25–August 27, 1995.

Produced by the Department of Publications
The Museum of Modern Art, New York
Osa Brown, Director of Publications
Edited by Mel Byars
Designed by Eric Baker Design Associates
Resin cover designed and executed by Gaetano Pesce and Pesce, Ltd.
Production by Marc Sapir
Printed by Litho, Inc., St. Paul
Bound by Midwest Editions, Inc., Minneapolis

Library of Congress Catalogue Card Number 95-075535
ISBN 0-87070-131-2 (MoMA, special cover)
ISBN 0-87070-132-0 (MoMA/T&H, paperbound)
ISBN 0-8109-6145-8 (Abrams, paperbound)

Published by The Museum of Modern Art
11 West 53 Street, New York, New York 10019

Paperbound edition distributed in the United States and Canada by
Harry N. Abrams, Inc., New York, A Times Mirror Company

Paperbound edition distributed outside the United States and Canada by
Thames & Hudson, Ltd., London

Printed in the United States

Contents

Many centuries ago, medieval alchemists sought to discover a way to transmute base materials, such as lead, into silver and gold. While they desired the riches such knowledge might reap, the alchemists also sought to understand the underlying structures of the material world.

In the late twentieth century, the transmutation of materials is no longer a goal but a reality. The advancements in our ability to analyze and manipulate the molecular structures of materials have created a whole new genre of well-designed objects.

Commenting on atomic theory, the noted physicist Richard P. Feynman remarked that one had to lose one's common sense in order to perceive what happens at the atomic level. So, too, must viewers of the exhibition *Mutant Materials in Contemporary Design* lose their common sense—a broad awareness of traditional materials, such as wood, metal, and glass—when considering "mutant materials": fabrics made from ceramics, windows that are alternatively clear and translucent, or plastics woven into the most durable of materials.

The exhibition and this book, which accompanies it, were prepared under unusually tight time constraints by Paola Antonelli, Associate Curator in The Museum of Modern Art's Department of Architecture and Design. Her admirable efforts provide an exciting opportunity to look at and understand the complicated new physical world of objects conceived by an international array of contemporary designers and manufactured with a surprising diversity of new materials.

Terence Riley
Chief Curator
Department of Architecture and Design

Introduction

The word "mutant" conjures images of Ninja Turtles, murderous carrots, and giant ants, either generated by radioactive explosions and experiments gone awry or sent to earth from the border of the galaxy to destroy our species. But it can also recall an imaginary race of beautiful extraterrestrial beings, who can at will, and from need, temporarily turn into almost anything—a lion, a cockroach, a bird of paradise—and still remain true to themselves. Change is their power and truth, unity and diversity their real character.

Today, this mutational power also belongs to ceramics, plastics, and glass, to name just three of the many materials used in contemporary design. Materials no longer have the appearance they had in the past. Engineers have endowed them with the power of change and caused them to be reborn as infant mutants of their elderly selves. In this book and the exhibition it accompanies, the materialization of the objects illustrated here is explored within this new historical perspective. Plastics can be as clear as glass, as sharp-edged as stone, and as metallic as aluminum (figure 1). Aluminum can look like quicksilver; wood can look like plastic. Scientists have discovered how to rearrange the molecules of matter into materials that not only appear different from those of the past but also have personalities and behaviors that are distinctly new. Solid metals are being replaced by ceramics and sheet metal by carbon fibers; wood can be as soft as upholstery. New technologies are being used to customize, extend, and modify the physical properties of materials and invent new ones. Materials are being transformed from adjuncts in passive roles to active interpreters of the goals of engineers and designers.

In only the past few decades, the impressive evolution of design materials and their technology has spawned a new material culture—one that is complex and in a state of continuous change and adaptation. This culture is global and is supported by the speed of information dissemination and by an international market of informed customers. It is animated by the visions of internationally trained designers and based on customization and variety. This new culture is nourished by the vitality of scientists' ingenuity, encouraged by industry, and aimed at designing more new customized materials.

The design of materials is not a new discovery. Ceramics and glass are millennia old; even plastics have been around for more than a century. Yet, by closely examining these three historically designed materials as case studies, a revolution is revealed. Ceramics and glass are the oldest of these, but in the twentieth century experimentation has laid open their unexpected mutant temperaments. Ceramics have a long history of a dual personality, split between strictly functional applications, such as spark plugs, electrical switches, and heavy-duty housewares, and the

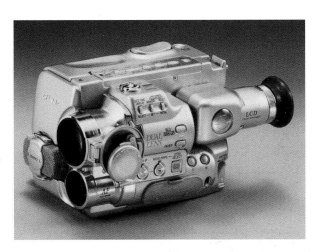

Figure 1. Fumitoshi Sakata, Seiji Kurokawa, and Tetsuya Tsujimura of TV and Video Systems Design Center. "Twin Cam 8mm Camcorder VL-MX7U." 1991 (1990). ABS, aluminum, and other materials; 4 x 4^1/2 x 7^3/4" (10 x 11 x 19 cm). Manufactured by Sharp Corporation, Japan. The plastic body is molded and colored to resemble aluminum.

decorative arts. In the eighteenth century, Josiah Wedgwood established specialization in his factories in order to separate the production of either "useful" or "beautiful" pottery. Recently, ceramic materials have become the protagonists of major scientific advancements—many say, the protagonists for years to come. Engineers have enhanced their traditional strength, hardness, and resistance to extreme temperatures and corrosion. New ceramics manufacturing processes, such as the direct transformation from powder to solid through sintering, take advantage of high temperature and pressure to form long-lasting cutting blades (figure 2), turbine rotors, nearly invisible dental braces, filaments in heat-resistant clothing and bullet-proof vests, and the famed insulating tiles of the space shuttle. These breakthrough technologies, although still very expensive, have already been embraced by some designers. The most important advances are found in superconductors, ceramic materials that are an insulant at ambient temperatures and conduct electricity without dissipation at very low temperatures, thus making the production of energy much more economical.[1] Their discovery is still relatively new and may not have an immediate design application.

Ceramics are thus a good example of a mutant material. They are hard and fragile. They can assume the functions and forms of metals and plastics. They are the oldest and newest, most innovative materials. They perform combinations of tasks once unthinkable and can be shaped in many forms, from the most rational and functional to the most arbitrary. Yet ceramics no longer have an absolute form but, rather, depend on the ideas of designers and engineers.

Glass, similar to ceramics but completely noncrystalline, has maintained through thirty-five centuries an image of transparency, fragility, and luminosity. To lend it strength and heat resistance, Carl Zeiss developed the first borosilicate glass in 1884. This invention gave birth in 1915 to Pyrex® kitchenware and chemical-laboratory equipment manufactured by Corning Glass Works. Purity still means strength; the purer the glass, the more improved its performance. According to Corning, the best glass is simple fused silica, obtained through the flame-hydrolysis process developed in 1952. Used in astronomy and space applications, the glass remains stable and flawlessly transparent even when thick. For further specialization, titanium is added to produce ultra-low-expansion (ULE) glass.

By its nature, glass has always invited alchemy, hybridization, and the infusion of different substances to achieve different personalities. Some of the most successful of a vast number of experiments have occurred in the twentieth century. Glass ceramics, also developed by Corning under the name Pyroceram®, were first used in nose cones (radomes) for guided missiles and beginning in 1958 were formed into numerous domestic objects, including tableware. A type of glass ceramic perfected in 1970 is machinable with conventional steel or carbide tools, and other recent advancements have made catalytic converters in automobiles possible.

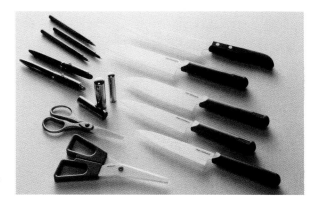

Figure 2. Fine Ceramics Division of Kyocera Corporation. Kitchen Knives and Scissors with Zirconia Blades; Ballpoint Pens with Ceramic Balls. 1984 (1983). Manufactured by Kyocera Corporation, Japan.

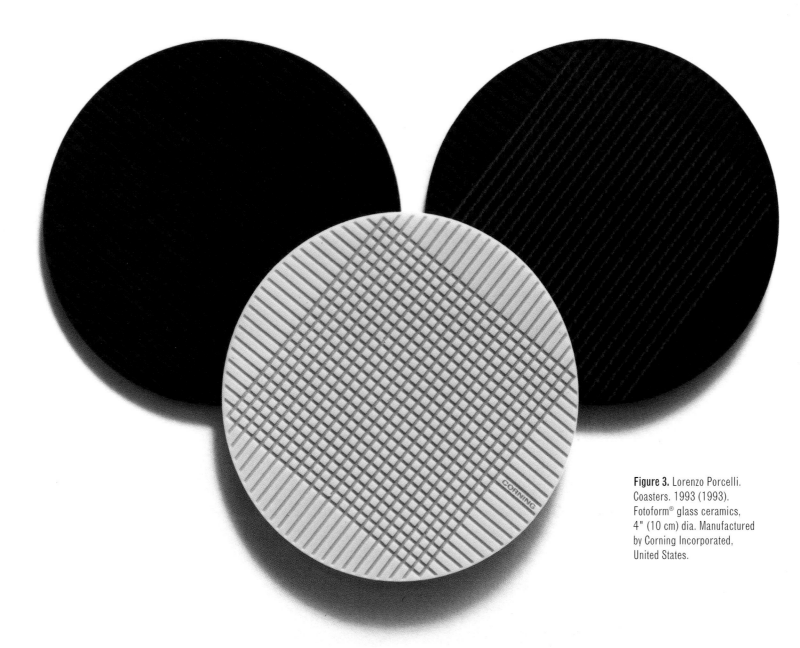

Figure 3. Lorenzo Porcelli.
Coasters. 1993 (1993).
Fotoform® glass ceramics,
4" (10 cm) dia. Manufactured
by Corning Incorporated,
United States.

Through experimentation with other additives, Corning engineers
produced photosensitive glass, realized as Fotalite™ in 1949, Fotoform®
in 1951, and Fotoceram® in 1953. This glass is photographically impressed and
acid-etched, and it can even be converted to a crystalline ceramic material
(figure 3). Corning also developed optical glass (1942); later, by adding lead,
radiation controlling glass; chemically strengthened glass, which bends at a
flexural strength of 100,000 lbs./sq. in. (70 kg/sq. mm); and photochromic glass
(1964), which changes color on exposure to light. Other inventions have included
coatings on glass sheets, which become nonsticking, polarized, or electrically
conductive. A newly developed (by Viracon and 3M, among others) sandwich of
glass sheets and liquid crystals becomes opaque for privacy when the crystals
are agitated by the flick of an electrical switch. The development of new
manufacturing processes led to the production of optical fibers, the information
carriers of today, and of perfectly pure liquid-crystal displays. These are
dramatically poured using natural gravity and are cooled and cut in the process.
Glass can be a magnifying lens, a telescope mirror (figure 4), and a kitchen
cooking pan that looks like ceramic. It can act like a metal or a plastic. The
narrative and the possibilities for glass, like ceramics, are almost endless.

"Plastics" is a label as all-encompassing as "species." Plastics are divided
into subgroups of families, defined either by composition (polyurethanes and
silicones) or by technology (thermoplastics and thermosetting materials). Each

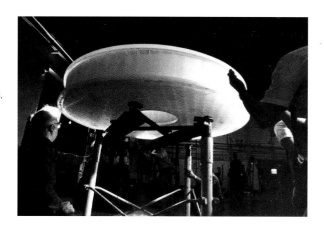

Figure 4. Corning Technical Products Division. Hubble Space Telescope Mirror Blank. 1990 (c. 1978). ULE glass, 8' (2.4 m) dia. Manufactured by Corning Incorporated, United States.

subgroup is made up of materials with names that would sound appropriate in a science-fiction movie, such as Rynite® (by Du Pont), Xenoy® (by GE Plastics), or Victrex® (by ICI). So much has changed since French philosopher Roland Barthes cursed plastics in 1957: "Despite names that would suit a Greek shepherd (polystyrene, phenoplast, polyvinyl, polyethylene) . . . this is a graceless material, lost between the exuberance of rubber and the flat hardness of metal. . . . Its noise undoes as do its colors, for it seems capable of acquiring only the most chemical colors; it retains only the most aggressive forms of yellow, red, and green."[2]

The story of plastics is like the story of a smart but troubled person: wishing to imitate grown-ups during childhood, getting into ideological and political trouble during youth, acquiring flexibility and a quiet beauty during the mature years. When Barthes encountered these polymers,[3] they were in their most offensive adolescence, and he had little patience for them.

In 1862 the British inventor Alexander Parkes created his eponymous Parkesine to simulate ivory; made with nitrocellulose, it was softened by vegetable oil and camphor. Then seven years later came Celluloid, highly inflammable and a good substitute for tortoiseshell. Bakelite followed, as did many other plastics. At the beginning of the twentieth century, plastics were used only in small objects as a surrogate for precious natural materials and had no truth of their own. PVC (polyvinyl chloride), created in 1927, was followed by Barthes's other "Greek shepherds": polystyrene (1929), polymethyl methacrylate, polyethylene, and unsaturated polyester resins (1933), polyurethane (1937), Nylon and polytetrafluoroethylene or Teflon™ (1938), PET/polyester (polyethylene terephthalate; 1941), high-density polyethylene (1953), polypropylene (1954)— and the list goes on.

In the late 1950s, plastics exploded in a burst of emancipation: the time for plastics, the flashy, exuberant materials that Barthes so vehemently despised, to show their new truth was at hand (figure 5). If the 1950s had witnessed the demise of imitation and a leap in structural scale, the 1960s initiated political involvement. The plastic object became a political symbol—serially produced, uniformly inexpensive, and equally available to all social classes (figure 6)—and signified economy and democracy through the 1970s.[4] Designers and architects celebrated the Age of Thermoplastics with suffocating global environments (see page 8), and plastics collapsed from overexposure. Soon, they had become a politically incorrect symbol of the threat to the environment, and in the 1980s a new generation of consumers, whose bourgeois tastes they could not at first meet, cast them out. Wisdom came with maturity, or maybe it was resignation. In order to survive in the post-industrial world, plastics have had to abandon ideology. Differentiated series and more refined compositions have given plastics an aura of exclusivity. Their

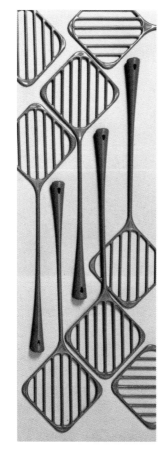

Figure 5. Gino Colombini. Carpet Beaters. 1959 (1959). Polyethylene and harmonic wire reinforcement, 24 x 7" (60 x 15 cm). Manufactured by Kartell S.p.a., Italy.

marriage with steel and aluminum in chairs and tables has made them more acceptable for the home. The development of new tooling and additive formulas improved the texture of plastics and presented new structural possibilities. Enhanced recycling abilities came to terms with political correctness.

Plastics Handbook[5] lists thirty-seven groups of resins and compounds, divided into subgroups. Among them, thermosetting polymers and injection-molded thermoplastics are perhaps the two largest categories. Thermosetting polymers, most often available in soft, acrid-smelling sheets or as liquids, reach a permanent set state when heated. Injection-molded thermoplastics (figure 7), furnished as granular raw materials, are heat-melted, injected into a mold, and solidified by temperature reduction. But plastic materials can also be blow-molded, extruded, cast, or formed.

Plastics have had and will have many lives in millions of forms. Since their invention, they have represented the materialization of ideas, particularly so today. Yet the best example of the revolution of materials is the experimentation with composites, one of the important chapters in the history of twentieth-century technology (see figure 8). Composites are combinations of materials and of their

Figure 6. Polyethylene ice-cube bags.

Figure 7. Anna Castelli Ferrieri. "4870" Chair. 1985 (1985). Polypropylene. Manufactured by Kartell S.p.a., Italy. The opening of a steel mold after injection and cooling.

individual properties. The most frequently used composites are combinations of glass or carbon fibers and resins. Lightweight and resistant to corrosion because of the resin, and strong and flexible owing to fibers, composites have revolutionized the manufacture of a wide range of objects (figure 9), including sports equipment, automobiles, and airplanes.

All advanced materials, old and new, have been invented to meet practical needs. Innovative materials and techniques are usually tested by large, progressive industries but sometimes by small, experimental, independent groups. Military engineers and surfers test advanced materials in specific applications; designers then apply their findings to the development of everyday objects. The design industry has facilitated the introduction of new materials into domestic life. For example, in the 1950s, Charles and Ray Eames adapted fiberglass, used in the manufacture of radar-detecting aircraft nose cones during World War II, to chair design.[6] Donald Chadwick and William Stumpf's more recent "Aeron" chair (see page 56) was derived from the interior structure of automobile seating, and Richard Sapper and Samuel Lucente's "Leapfrog" computer (see page 64) was inspired by the materials used for the "Stealth" F-117A fighter aircraft.

Engineers' demands have grown in number and sophistication in order to solve practical problems often foreign to everyday life, including technologies to enable man to walk on the moon and to disintegrate missile factories detected by satellites. Engineers are devising methods to infuse intelligence and memory into materials that will actively satisfy the sense of necessity and economy that has been fostered by an awareness of the planet's limited resources. This ambition was summarized by the Japanese Science and Technology Agency in 1983: "To develop materials with specific functions—optical, electromagnetic, chemical, biological, thermal, and electronic."[7] The goal is to defeat entropy with these highly resistant and adaptable information carriers. As with computers, automobiles, and even employees in a firm, materials are expected to perform.

Figure 8. Stephen Armellino. Bullet-resistant Mask. 1983 (1983). Kevlar® and polyester resin, 11 x 6 3/4 x 4" (28 x 17.2 x 10 cm). Manufactured by American Body Armor & Equipment, Inc., United States. The Museum of Modern Art, New York, gift of the manufacturer.

Figure 9. Ciba Heath Tecna Aerospace Co. Windpower Blade. 1994 (1994). Fiberglass in epoxy resin, 52 x 7' (16.5 x 2.1 m). Manufactured by Ciba for Kenetech Windpower, United States.

Studies in contemporary materials are conducted to develop their easy machinability, thus saving energy. For example, so-called soft glass melts at lower temperatures than other glasses; light metal alloys can be formed at lower temperatures than other metals throughout the manufacturing process. These materials are expected to last longer, reduce waste, and be more reliable and more resistant to corrosion, erosion, and wear. Their manufacture and use are often guided by CAD (computer-aided design) and CAM (computer-aided manufacturing) programs, which maximize performance by simulating in advance the manufacturing process, thus exposing possible flaws in production and minimizing scrap waste. Contemporary materials behave as materials never have before. Superplastic ultra-high-carbon steel can be stretched to about ten times its original length before structural failure occurs. Some materials are made antiseptic for use in prosthetic devices; others, endowed with high or low memories, adapt to extreme physical changes and then return to their initial forms (figure 10). Memory and intelligence, the most desirable qualities materials can possess, are also useful in product design. When foams have memory, they can remember the shape of our feet in ski boots and the contour of our backs in the lumbar support of chairs. Some metal alloys used in brassieres remember women's breast shapes unless stretched over six percent; eyeglass frames can now spring back to their original forms after they have been bent; other metal objects, once deformed, recover their shapes when heated.[8] In Japan, fabrics of pure cotton and silk are treated with polyester resin in shape-memory ties and shirts that need no ironing. Labels change color on supermarket food packaging to indicate when the storage time has expired or the temperature is too high. Japan also produces some of the most advanced ceramics and a "sea-gel" foam, lighter than air and biodegradable, for use in the disposal of nuclear waste.[9]

Contemporary materials are studied to develop combinations of qualities, as is most evident in the technology of composites. Engineers have turned to alchemy in their search for the perfect mutant material—the dream material that is a synthesis of the best qualities in all other materials, including mutability—and designers have begun to adopt these new technologies. Engineers have long been familiar with the dimensions of pagan alchemy, but, until only a few decades ago, designers and architects believed in the absolute truth of materials. They believed that each material, even designed fiberglass and ceramics, had an expressive soul enhanced by its physical properties and by the techniques of its manufacture. A set of finite relationships had formed since the nineteenth century into an almost religious code of reference: glass meant a blown, cast, or plated transparency; steel meant a poured, tubular, or planar tenacity (figure 11); wood meant a solid, bent, or laminated flexibility (figure 12); ceramics meant a cast

Figure 10. Ron Arad. "Transformer" Sofa. 1983 (1983). PVC and polystyrene pellets. Manufactured by Brainos, Great Britain. Air is removed from the polyethylene bag and the shape of the body remains carved in the sofa.

hardness and fragility. Designers, craftsmen, and architects obsessively sought a truth that, when revealed, would guide them toward a harmony of means and goals and thus toward perfection in design.

The historical quest for truth in materials, exalted by the Arts and Crafts movement, was also pursued, for example, in expressionist architecture, as illustrated by the extraordinary utopia envisioned in Paul Scheerbart's 1914 book *Glasarchitektur*.[10] Scheerbart chose glass as the paradigmatic material for a global design ethic and aesthetic—a metaphor for an immaculate, democratic world. In Finland in the twentieth century many generations of designers and architects have been investigating a singular indigenous material—wood— through the technology of laminating and bending (figure 13), and the examination continues today. The masters and pupils of the modern movement embraced tubular steel as the manifestation of their ideas about the world, as expressed through furniture design. The Eameses' use in the 1950s of the newly conceived fiberglass, even though experimental and innovative, displays a faith in the material and a philosophical approach similar to their earlier attitude toward natural wood: an exploration of the material to learn from it not only about structure and function but also about form and beauty.

Displays of faith reached plastics last and were somewhat tainted by excessive enthusiasm and often intense, uncritical devotion. Ironically, plastics were also the materials to initiate a crisis of doubt and to support the postmodern

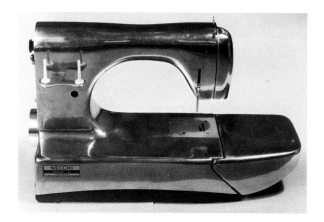

Figure 11. Marcello Nizzoli. "Mirella" Sewing Machine. 1957 (1957). Steel. Manufactured by Necchi, Italy. The steel body of the machine before it is painted.

Figure 12. Carved wood pieces at a Ceccotti manufacturing plant, Italy.

era's uncertain cultural and aesthetic references. It is interesting to speculate on what new forms elastomers and carbon fibers will suggest to designers.

Revolutions in science, technology, and philosophy are historically accompanied by deep, unconscious parallel shifts in the culture at large. A significant turn has come to pass in the culture of architectural and industrial design. The deconstructivist theories of French poststructuralist philosophers such as Jean Baudrillard and Jacques Derrida have been widely disseminated, particularly in intellectual circles and in the press, along with more cryptic scientific theories (like that of chaos) and mathematical formulations (for instance, fractal geometry) formulated from empirical observations of reality. A brand of amorality and cynicism has characterized the postmodern attitude: most of us easily accept both one principle and its opposite, so long as the juxtaposition is meaningful and witty. Society today has been taught to appreciate creative deceptions and to value and welcome diversity and change. Mutant materials suit this new world.

Truth in materials is no longer an absolute and unique concept. Contemporary designers are facing the challenge of defining its new multifaceted manifestations. The mutant character of materials, as expressive as it is functional and structural, generates new forms and a more experimental approach toward design.

In the following pages are selected objects in which the designers, mastering their use of mutant materials, express the technical and formal possibilities through an innovative, contemporary language. Yet the presentation does not presume to define in detail the new material culture, still too close for codification. The sequencing of the materials was inspired by scientific convention and expressive considerations. For example, glass and ceramics, often grouped together, are separated because of their very different resultant applications. Even though foam and elastomers are plastics, a division between soft and hard synthetic polymers tends to support this general thesis. Recycled materials coexist with their parent materials. They have not been given a separate category, in order to emphasize that recycling is a given and that our focus is economy of thought and design.

The goal is to offer an insight into the new relationship between designers and materials. The objects chosen are diverse, and some exploit materials in a manner that may seem limited in that only function is a concern. The logical beauty of sports and medical equipment best illustrates the power of change brought about by mutant materials and the explosion of customized hybrids and composites. Other objects serve as more sophisticated examples of the aesthetic uses of mutant materials: surprisingly soft areas on the same hard-plastic element, and video cameras and fishing reels in reinforced plastics disguised as metals. Considered as a group, the objects portray a material culture based on arbitrariness—an aesthetic centered on individualism and continuing research.

These objects also reveal procedural problems. Some new materials appear to have momentarily outgrown our needs, as computers have outgrown the speed of our thoughts and fingers. A carbon-fiber chair is still too lightweight and its high-tech appearance too peculiar for acceptance by a wide public. Profound changes in lifestyles do not occur overnight. We have become accustomed to wineglasses and eyeglass frames that do not break, and to artificial "creatures"—such as computer mouses, remote controls, and food mixers—that offer convenience and populate our daily lives. For cold weather, we buy garments made of recycled plastic bottles. Furnishings in carbon fiber may soon be as familiar as these other synthetics in the domestic landscape.

In the introductory stage, an advanced material is designed and modified to serve a specific purpose. In the transfer stage, its strict, economical concept is expanded, energizing the discovery of other, more general—even universal—uses. An ideal contemporary material is meant to be lasting, easily recycled, reusable, noninvasive, and more flexible. Its sensible application may incorporate the old within the new, making good use of past intellectual and technical achievements. The new material culture has made designers more responsible in the name of environmental and conceptual economy. In this view, designers and engineers are seen as full collaborators in the development and application of new materials.

Ezio Manzini plays a semantic game in his book *The Material of Invention*,[11] one of the inspirations behind this project. While the Latin *invenire* means "to find," Manzini asserts that a "material of invention" is no longer a "found material" but rather one that is calculated and engineered to achieve a specific performance. And we may add, if the point of departure for design was once the material itself, today it is the mutable quality of materials. If this is so, designers must return to ground zero, where doubt is the basis of discovery. The mastery of today's designed materials requires as much ingenuity as the mastery

Figure 13. Tapio Wirkkala. Platter. c. 1951. Carved, laminated plywood block.

of nature's gifts did in the past. The focus, too, is the same, and that is process: in this case, the exploration of advanced technologies by informed designers and their application by manufacturers equipped with intelligent machines.

William Duncan, author of *Manufacturing 2000*, has predicted: "The single most important material used by manufacturers in the future will be data. . . . At some point many years down the road, the raw materials will be chemical 'slurries' and raw elements that may be assembled and reassembled or restructured in replication processes."[12] The ultimate goal of developing a material that can be instantaneously designed, manufactured, and customized for and by the end user poses an interesting paradox, since in the process the role of the designer will be substantially redefined. In the future, the focus of design may no longer be the creation of the discrete object but the formulation of possibilities.

Figure 14. Rita McBride. *Toyota.* 1990. Rattan, 4'2" x 15' x 5'9" (127 x 457.2 x 175.3 cm). Museum of Contemporary Art, San Diego, extended loan and promised gift of Michael and Brenda Sandler.

Notes

1. Metallic superconductors have been studied since 1911, but they were effectively produced at only very low temperatures, near 0° K. or −459°F. (−273°C.). The studies of ceramic superconductors achieved a level of great success in 1985. Since then, the experimentation with various rare powders and oxides, such as yttrium, has made higher and higher working temperatures possible, with the goal being ambient temperatures.

2. Roland Barthes, "Le Plastique," in *Mythologies* (Paris: Editions du Seuil, 1957).

3. A polymer is a macromolecular material. Plastics are formed by joining together long chains of small groups of atoms, known as monomers. Some plastics are composed of macromolecules about 100,000 atoms in size. See Bryan Bunch and Alexander Hellemans, eds., *The Timetables™ of Technology* (New York: Touchstone/Simon & Schuster, 1993), p. 343.

4. *The Story of Plastics* (London: Design Museum, 1994), brochure.

5. *Plastics Handbook* (New York: McGraw-Hill, n.d.), n.p.

6. In 1937 Corning Glass Works perfected Fiberglas® as a proprietary composite. The material consists of a resin matrix reinforced with embedded glass fibers.

7. E. D. Hondros, "Materials, Year 2000," in Tom Forester, ed., *The Materials Revolution: Superconductors, New Materials, and the Japanese Challenge* (Cambridge, Mass.: MIT Press, 1988), p. 62.

8. The recovery is the result of a change, known as a thermo-elastic-martensitic transformation, in the crystalline structure of an alloy. The shape-memory characteristic of alloys was first discovered in 1932 when gold and cadmium were mixed. The nickel-titanium combination (Nitinol) was developed by W. Buehler in 1962 and applied by NASA to the manufacture of a satellite antenna that unfolds when heated with electrical current (Bunch and Hellemans, pp. 351 and 395).

9. Juli Capella and Quim Larrea, "Compuestos del Futuro," *Babelia* (July 2, 1994), p. 25.

10. Paul Scheerbart, *Glasarchitektur* (Berlin: Verlag der Sturm, 1914).

11. Ezio Manzini, *The Material of Invention* (Cambridge, Mass.: MIT Press, 1989); first pub. as *La Materia dell'invenzione* (Milan: Arcadia/Progetto Cultura Montedison, 1986).

12. William L. Duncan, *Manufacturing 2000* (New York: AMACOM, 1994), p. 203.

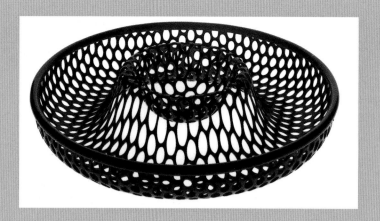

Plastics represent the distance that a century of technological progress has put between craftsmanship and industrialization. Polymers are the artificial materials *par excellence* and can only be formed in a malleable state. Unfortunately, the production processes almost always require expensive tools. Among the exceptions are polyurethane resins, which are cured at ambient temperatures and shaped with simple composite or wood molds. For example, a composite mold was used in the manufacture of Bob Evans's swimming fins (page 23). But the processing of polymers often involves a more costly and complex technology. Nevertheless, today's manufacturers have been able to achieve some degree of freedom within a specific production cycle in order to create more distinctive objects and better satisfy market needs. In addition, computer-aided design and computer-aided manufacturing (CAD/CAM) programs simulate the flow of the materials in the molds and predict the final outcome prior to production; they are a virtual-reality version of the craftsman's exploratory work and mitigate the burden of industrialization.

Injection molding—suitable for the most common polymers, such as polystyrene, high-density polyethylene, polypropylene, and ABS—is the most frequently employed technology. Objects are produced one at a time from granules that are liquified under heat and pressure and injected into steel molds. Similarly, continuous techniques, such as calendering and extrusion, employ open-ended molds, and blow or rotational molding forms objects through centrifugal pressure, which causes the plastic material to adhere to the mold walls. When the raw material is furnished in sheets, forming is accomplished by applying air or vacuum pressure to the heated sheets, or by drawing them through a press. Enzo Mari's "Atollo" fruit bowl (above) is an example of a vacuum-formed sheet.

Plastics can be liquefied to embrace their past lives and mix with other materials. Resins become matrixes in combination with the fibers of carbon, glass, or ceramics to form new advanced composites. They can also be combined with less noble, reused materials, such as the shredded fabrics in Gaetano Pesce's armchair and ottomans (page 43), and the wood dust and wood particles used in the plastic compounds on page 40. Plastics can be fully recycled, and their scars can even be used as aesthetic features, like those in the "Plaky" table (page 42).

No matter how advanced and automated the technologies may have become in the development of plastics into objects, manual intervention is still required. With some few exceptions, plastic objects are all finished, painted, or coated by hand. The craftsman has not yet disappeared and may indeed always be with us.

Plastics

Laura Handler (American, b. 1954), Dennis Decker (American, b. 1954), and Amanda Hong Magalhaes (American, b. 1968). "Gallery Glass" Goblets. 1993 (1992). Manufactured by Metrokane, Inc., United States.

Die-cast ultrasonic-sealed acrylic resin, two sizes: 5 1/2 h. x 4 3/4" dia. (14 h. x 12 cm dia.) and 7 3/4 h. x 3 3/4" dia. (19.7 h. x 9.5 cm dia.).

Laura Handler's studio specializes in the design of luxury items, such as perfume flacons and fine tableware, that often incorporate silver, crystal, and Bakelite. When challenged to use a poorly regarded material for drinking glasses (above), the Handler studio staff was able to elevate acrylic resin to a noble status. Three different-colored layers of plastic, molded separately, are sealed together by high-frequency sound waves, and an air bubble in the base is added as an ironic reference to lead crystal.

Bausch & Lomb Product Development. "Killer Loop™ Xtreme Pro" Sunglasses. 1994 (1994). Manufactured by Bausch & Lomb, Inc., United States.

DiamondHard™ (amorphous-diamond) coating on die-cast polycarbonate lenses and Megol® elastomer, 2¹/₄ x 6¹/₈ x 3" (5.7 x 15.5 x 7.5 cm).

The polycarbonate of the "Killer Loop Xtreme Pro" sunglasses (left) is coated with Bausch & Lomb's DiamondHard material, also known as DLC (diamondlike carbon). DLC, one of the hardest materials known, can be applied in thicknesses from .5 to 5 microns (a micron is one-hundred-millionth of a centimeter). The DLC coating, which renders the surface resistant to scratching, chemicals, and water and makes it hermetically sealed, is applied to optical products such as bar-code scanner windows and reflective mirrors; medical devices; and joint implants. The coating is accomplished by the ion-beam deposition process. Since the surface is remote from the plasma of accelerated carbon and hydrocarbon ions, it remains at an almost ambient temperature, which makes it possible to apply the technology to thermoplastics in addition to metals, ceramics, and glass. The technology has been patented by the Monsanto Company, Diamonex, Inc.

Bob Evans (American, b. 1950). "Tan Delta Force Fin®." 1994 (1994). Manufactured by Bob Evans Designs, Inc., United States.

Liquid-cast heat-cured Uniroyal flexible polyurethane, dimensions vary.

The "Force Fin" (left) is an example of highly efficient water-sports equipment as well as a poetic design statement. The innovative design was first conceived a decade ago by Bob Evans, an underwater photographer who derived it from observing the form and behavior of fish fins. As a result, the fins have the kind of economy of purpose found in nature, a union of shape and content. Evans chose liquid polyurethane resin for its elastic properties, or "memory." The integral design harnesses the dynamic, elastic power of the human body: as a swimmer kicks down, the blade opens up to take advantage of the full thrust, garnering the leg muscles as a force against the water and propelling the swimmer forward. In the downstroke, the blade assumes its original shape, propelling the swimmer forward again while assisting the upward recovery posture of a person's natural two-stroke kicking rhythm. During recovery, the tip of the fin folds downward, channeling the water flow behind it and easing the upward movement of the blade, thus anticipating the leg motion in the next sequential downward thrust. The dynamic engineering design came about through the use of a composite mold for casting polyurethane. This composite tooling, a recent and more agile alternative to costly metal molds, offers wide-ranging experimental possibilities.

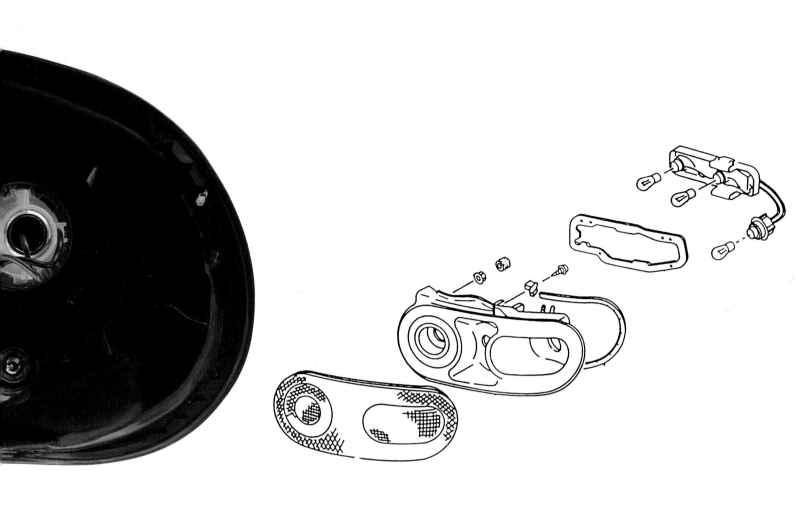

Mazda Motor Corporation. "MX5 Miata" Automobile Taillight. 1988 (1983). Manufactured by Mazda Motor Corporation, Japan.

Double-shot injection-molded acrylic-resin lens, injection-molded polypropylene reflector, and other materials; 5 3/4 x 13 3/4" (14.6 x 34.7 cm).

The Mazda design and engineering team took on the challenge of developing an automobile taillight in the smallest size and the least possible weight while meeting global standards and regulations and satisfying the aesthetic and economic demands of producing an affordable sports car. The team envisioned a thoroughly integrated object whose manufacture would incorporate sophisticated tooling and assembly machinery. Mazda's diagram (above) reveals the complex array of single parts assembled by a very simple factory operation, resulting in a lighting component which weighs less than 2 lbs. (.9 kg). Thanks to double-shot injection-molding technology, the color portions of the lens, except

for the round reflector, are produced in one mold. Since the amber portion for the turn indicator is molded within the red background area, the engineers had to alter the translucency of the injected acrylic resin to achieve the desired chromatic effect. The red lens was altered from an average translucency of 25% to 20%, and the amber lens from 65% to 46%. The lens surface is subtly bowed beyond the surface of the auto body, like a cabochon.

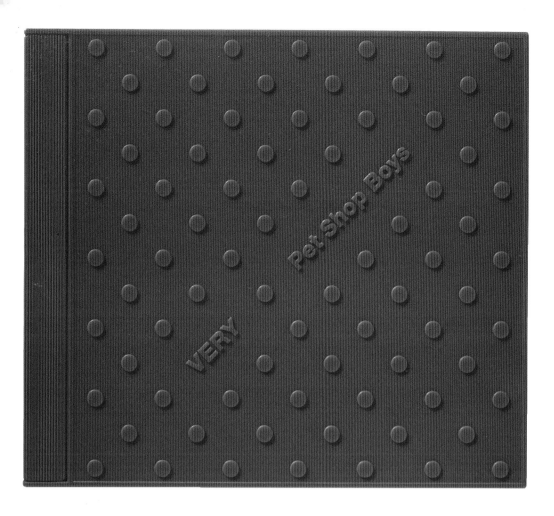

Daniel Weil (British, b. Argentina 1953) of Pentagram Design. Compact-Disc Packaging for *Very* Album by Pet Shop Boys. 1993 (1993). Manufactured by EMI Records, Great Britain. Injection-molded polystyrene, 5 x 5 1/2 x 1/2" (12.5 x 14 x 1.5 cm).

Pet Shop Boys, a leading British pop-music group, commissioned Daniel Weil to design a compact-disc case for their *Very* album. The injection-molded polystyrene case not only holds and protects the compact disc and the accompanying literature but is also a distinctive object separate from its contents.

Gaetano Pesce (Italian, b. 1939). Table Made with Music. (1988). Prototype by Bernini S.p.a., Italy. Cured reactive-molded polyurethane resin and steel, 19 5/16 h. x 31 1/2" dia. (49 h. x 80 cm dia.).

The interpretive qualities of plastic are summoned by Gaetano Pesce in two one-of-a-kind tables molded by music. In their production, Pesce used a round plateau mold and a liquid resin, which has a catalyzing time of about twenty minutes. In the manufacturing process, approximately sixteen to twenty tubes were connected along the periphery of the plateau to an air compressor, which channeled in recorded musical sounds for added vibration. (For example, the music of the British rock band Pink Floyd was used in the first experiment.) The compressor was connected to the tubes, and the process began. Semi-catalyzed colored resins were agitated, mixed by the tubes, and aerated and puffed up by the vibrations of the pulsating music. Mixing and agitation continued until the resin solidified.

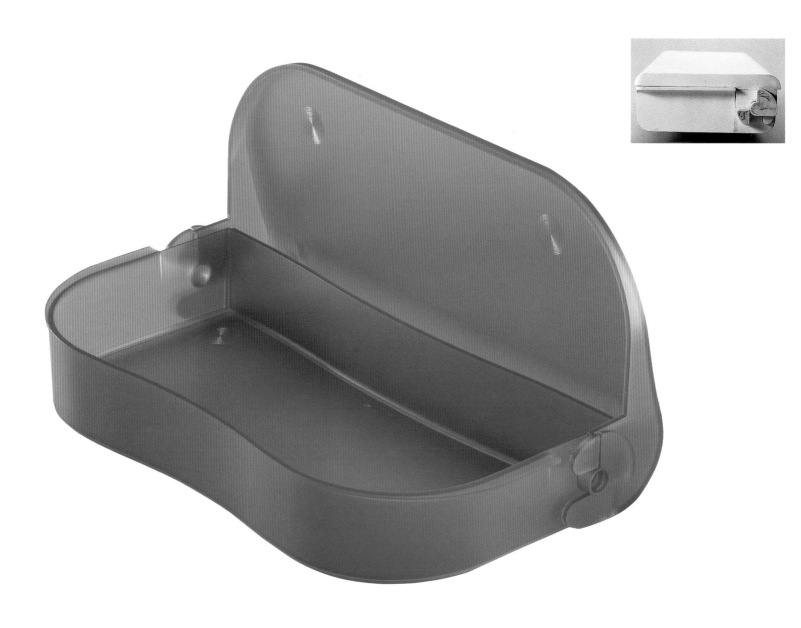

Enzo Mari (Italian, b. 1932). "Flores" Box. 1992 (1991).
Manufactured by Danese S.r.l., Italy.

Thermoplastic polymer,
6 x 12 1/4 x 3" (15 x 31 x 7.6 cm).

The small design-production company Danese was founded by Jacqueline Vodoz and Bruno Danese in 1957. For thirty-five years, in collaboration with designers Bruno Munari and Enzo Mari, pioneers Vodoz and Danese have explored the numerous hidden qualities of plastics, transforming the material into distinctive objects, at least equal to those in glass, ceramics, and steel. The "Flores" box illustrates plastic's elevated status. Elegant, precious, and, for a plastic object, expensive (about $50), the box is made of thermoplastic resin. The ingenious hinge eliminates the need for screws or other hardware. The polymer, unsuitable for angular shapes, is appropriate to form the box's curvilinear, organic shape and, in the black-and-white versions only, is shock- and flame-resistant.

Jasper Morrison (British, b. 1959). "Bottle" Storage Module. 1994 (1993). Manufactured by Magis S.r.l., Italy. Injection-molded polypropylene and anodized aluminum, 10 1/4 x 9 x 14 3/16" (26 x 23 x 36 cm).

Jasper Morrison, a champion of contemporary design purity, adroitly approached the design of a highly utilitarian object—a bottle storage unit—and transformed it into a handsome object. Morrison developed "Bottle" as a modest, practical interpretation of the traditional wine-storage system. Each module is built of four anodized aluminum tubes and two identical polypropylene sides. Since only one mold was used to make the plastic parts, tooling costs were reduced. The module—in clear, blue, orange, or green—is assembled by hand and, when filled with bottles, creates an interesting wall of light.

Antonio Citterio (Italian, b. 1950) and Glen Oliver Löw (German, b. 1959). "Mobil" Container System. 1994 (1993). Manufactured by Kartell S.p.a., Italy. Bulk-dyed thermoplastic polymer containers and chrome- or aluminum-colored steel frame and handles, various dimensions.

Modular storage was also the inspiration for Antonio Citterio and Glen Oliver Löw's "Mobil" container system. The drawers are integrated into a sleek, portable steel structure on casters. Available also in a polished and matte-finished thermoplastic material, the system is manufactured by Kartell, the pioneering plastics firm established by Giulio Castelli which has been producing domestic and laboratory goods since its founding in 1949.

Ross Lovegrove (British, b. 1958) of Studio X. "Figure of Eight" Side Chair. 1994 (1993). Manufactured by Cappellini S.p.a., Italy. Die-cast polyurethane seat, stainless-steel frame, and nylon feet; 30 3/4 x 19 3/4 x 21 1/4" (78 x 50 x 54 cm). The Museum of Modern Art, New York, gift of the manufacturer.

The geometry of Ross Lovegrove's sinuous side chair is based on the shape formed by a bent circular strip of paper; the shape is pinched at more or less the center, after which it is folded at a fixed angle of 105°. The preliminary form (above left) created by the designer in steel banding reveals the purity of action that he transformed into a continuous plastic surface whose ancillary support structure is understated, almost insignificant. The shell was molded from Baydur 6700Z, a polyurethane resin by Bayer that is furnished in tanks. Combined with a catalyst, the mixture is poured into a mold of steel, aluminum, or epoxy resin. The mold temperature is held at 140° to 170° F. (60° to 75° C.) for 90 to 120 seconds in order to produce a 1/2 in. (1.5 cm) thick, hardened section. The final chair shell is painted.

Bruno Ninaber van Eyben (Dutch, b. 1950) of Ninaber/Peters/Krouwel Industrial Design. Ruler. 1990 (1990). Manufactured by Randstad Uitzendbureau bv, The Netherlands. Injection-molded Tampoprinted (pad-printed) ABS (acrylonitrile-butadiene-styrene) and evoprene elastomer, 1 x 13 3/4 x 1/2" (4 x 35 x 1.5 cm).

The ruler designed by Dutch studio Ninaber/Peters/Krouwel is one item of a series of desktop accessories produced to enhance the image of Randstad, an agency for temporary workers. Its design is as basic and utilitarian as the object itself. Soft to the touch and in an ideal shape, the ruler, like a carpet, is raised at the edge as if someone were sweeping dust underneath. A thin line of evoprene rubber on the underside keeps the ruler from sliding when a line is drawn.

Mark Sanders (British, b. 1958). "No-Spill" Chopping Board. 1990 (1988). Manufactured by Rubycliff, Ltd., Great Britain. Injection-molded polypropylene, 15 1/4 x 8 3/4 x 1/4" (39 x 22 x .5 cm). The Museum of Modern Art, New York, gift of the designer.

The chopping board is an articulated, one-piece polypropylene slab. Lying flat as the food is chopped, the board folds into a chute to channel its contents directly into pots and pans, avoiding spills. The material was chosen for its surface resistance and mass strength, even when thinly formed with moveable sections. Yet the hinges, which are integrally molded with the slab, had to be thicker to resist knife cutting. When one hinge crosses another, only one can fold. The chopping board took five years to be developed. To achieve an effective tooling design, Mark Sanders used "mold flow" computer technology, which simulates injected-plastic flow on a computer screen and imitates the progression of mold filling. The hinges were subjected to a test of one million folds, and the cutting surface was exposed to the equivalent of two years of chopping, with no damage.

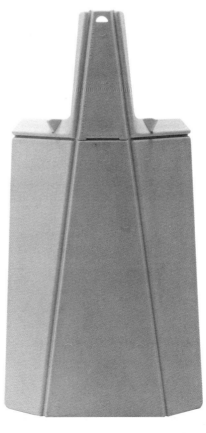

Ettore Sottsass's lipstick-red "Valentine" typewriter of 1969 is one of the finest examples of the kind of plastic objects that have entered our domestic environment in the last few decades as adorable, yet functional, tools. Their appearance has been encouraged by the ability of plastics to form technically sophisticated organic shapes. The computer mouse crawls across practically every office desk. These devices form an electronic interface between humans and machines.

Donald Carr (American, b. 1959) of AT&T Consulting Design Group. "PalmMouse" Computer Pointing Device. (1992). Prototype by AT&T Global Information Solutions Design Integrity Center, United States.

Injection-molded polycarbonate body, Santoprene® (low-density thermoplastic elastomeric rubber) saddle, and copper and acetate antenna; $3\,^1/_2$ x $2\,^1/_4$ x $1\,^3/_8$" (8.9 x 5.7 x 3.5 cm).

The "PalmMouse" is designed to be worn on the hand but can also be rolled on the thigh or on the armrest of a chair. Its designer, Donald Carr, calls it "wearable technology."

Paul Montgomery (American, b. 1959) and Herbert Pfeiffer (German. b. 1949). "MouseMan®" Cordless Computer Pointing Device. 1993 (1993). Manufactured by Logitech, Inc., United States.

Injection-molded ABS, $4\,^1/_8$ x $3\,^1/_8$ x $1\,^3/_8$" (10.5 x 8 x 3.5 cm).

Paul Montgomery and Herbert Pfeiffer's cordless "MouseMan" pointer uses low-frequency radio technology, with four transmission channels to avoid interference with other similar devices. Only the transmitter is shown here (left); a nondescript receiver box is connected to the computer processor unit (CPU). The body of the mouse prominently features finger indentations.

Christopher Loew (American, b. 1963), Lawrence Schubert (American, b. 1962), and Christopher Lada (American, b. 1952) of IDEO Product Development. "Proset" Professional Telephone Headset. 1993 (1991–92). Manufactured by Unex Corporation, United States.

Injection-molded ABS-polycarbonate blend, acetal, insert-molded thermoplastic elastomers, stainless steel, and brass; 7 x 2 3/4 x 2" (17.8 x 7 x 5 cm).

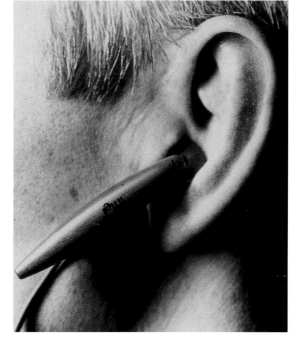

Stephen Peart (British, b. 1958) of Vent Design. "Enterprise" Earmounted Telephone Headset. 1993 (1993). Manufactured by Plantronics, Inc., United States.

Injection-molded polycarbonate and stamped metal, 2 7/16 x 3/8 x 5/6" (6.2 x 1 x 2 cm).

The "Proset" (above) and "Enterprise" (right) headsets are worn over and inside the ear, respectively. The former, by designers of the IDEO studio, features a microphone connected by wire to an organically shaped ear piece, oddly resembling the rotary telephone. Peart's "Enterprise" model has the appearance of an insect or coffee bean.

Paul Bradley (American, b. 1960) and Lawrence Lam (American, b. 1960) of IDEO Product Development. "3-D Mouse" Computer Pointing Device. 1991 (1991). Manufactured by Logitech, Inc., United States.

Injection-molded ABS, 6 x 4 1/4 x 3" (15 x 10.9 x 7.2 cm).

Paul Bradley and Lawrence Lam's "3-D Mouse," appropriate for CAD/CAM, animation, and virtual-reality applications, isolates and links points and areas in three-dimensional space. For a Cartesian coordinate, the pointing device uses ultrasonic speakers, placed in a triangular position on the CPU, and microphones to position itself. Signal pulses are transmitted at a rate of fifty per second.

Molded to fit the hand, the nutcracker, magnifier, and pliers enhance the expressive qualities of polymers. Plastic is not an obvious material of choice for these strong, durable, heavy-duty utilitarian objects.

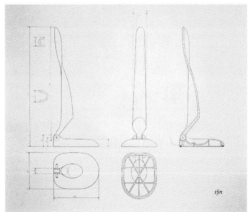

Giorgio Gurioli (Italian, b. 1957) and Francesco Scansetti (Italian, b.1955). "Noce™" Nutcracker. 1993 (1992). Manufactured by Outlook-Zelco Europe, S.r.l., Italy.

Injection-molded glass-reinforced nylon, 12 x 4 x 5" (30.5 x 10 x 12.5 cm).

Glass-filled nylon proved hard enough to break a nutshell, scratch-resistant enough to retain its finish, and flexible enough to bear the stress of the lever action. Strips of rubber are glued to the bottom for stability.

Gordon Randall Perry (American, b. 1943) and Richard Feinbloom (American, b. 1948). "ClearVision II" Hand-Held Magnifier. 1994 (1994). Manufactured by Designs For Vision, Inc., United States.

Die-cast urethane and glass, $13/16$ x $2^3/16$ x $6^7/16$" (2.1 x 5.5 x 16.6 cm).

The hand-held magnifier is cast of urethane from cast-aluminum molds. The large, comfortable, sturdy handle and frame provide an effective and reassuring grip even for weak, insecure hands.

Steve Visser (American, b. 1959), Miro Tasic (American, b. 1968), and Ashok Midha (Indian, b. 1946) of Purdue University. "Compliers" Flexural Fishing Pliers. (1992). Prototype. Injection-molded Delrin® (acetal-elastomer thermoplastic alloy), $2\,^3/_4 \times 9 \times ^3/_4$" (7 x 23 x 2 cm).

The integrated joints of the pliers' handle manipulate the rigid jaws, which are configured especially to remove hooks from fish. Formed in one piece, the mechanism uses the principle of variable mechanical advantage: the farther the handle closes, the firmer the grip on a hook.

Advances in molded-plastics technology have spawned a new expressiveness in silhouettes where mechanical details can be made curvilinear and amorphous. Ribs, articulations, teeth, and vents become features to be displayed rather than hidden. The structural effect overshadows the function to visually stimulating, scenographic ends.

Mark Stella (American), Kuni Masuda (Japanese), and Sohrab Vossoughi (Iranian) of Ziba Design. "World Class 300 Series" Fishing-Rod Spinning Reel. 1992 (1992). Manufactured by Fenwick, Inc., United States.

Injection-molded glass-filled nylon and spun aluminum, 4 x 3 13/16 x 5" (10.2 x 9.7 x 12.7 cm).

Ziba Design's lightweight fishing reel (left) looks like metal but is, in fact, injection-molded glass-filled nylon, and the line spool is spun aluminum. The movement of wriggling live bait is simulated by switching the wire bale back and forth from casting to lure-retrieval modes. The combination of flexibility and structural strength was made possible by the successful marriage of materials and process.

Rollerblade Research and Development and Nordica S.p.a. "Aeroblade® ABT®" In-line Skates. 1993 (1992). Manufactured by Rollerblade, Inc., United States.

BladeLite™ polyurethane shell, glass-reinforced nylon frame, foam padding, and other materials; dimensions vary.

On Aeroblade® in-line skates, the boot becomes an armature of the foot, and the wheels transform the body into a vehicle. The boot, composed of several parts, includes a variety of complex plastic elements for high-performance applications. The flexible, sleek polyurethane boot, molded in three asymmetrical, hinged segments, is sculpted and ventilated for lightness. The shell is attached to a frame of two-piece glass-reinforced nylon that offers rigidity and is fitted with an inner boot of multi-density foams and mesh, which incorporates an air-inflation component.

Naoto Fukasawa (Japanese, b. 1956), Tim Brown (British, b. 1962), and Paul Howard (American, b. 1955) of IDEO Product Development. Computer Processor Stand. 1991 (1990). Manufactured by Technology Molded Plastics (now Hartzell, Inc.), United States. Injection-molded high-impact polystyrene, 5 x 7 1/4 x 3 3/4" (12.7 x 18.4 x 9.5 cm) closed.

Articulated like the skates and fishing reel, yet in a matter-of-fact design determined by function only, the integral-plastic telescoping element of the computer processor stand expands from 7 1/4 in. to 10 in. (25.4 cm) to accommodate a range of CPUs that may weigh up to 55 lbs. (122.3 kg). Made of high-impact polystyrene, it provides a tough support that resists kicks.

Stefan Lindfors (Finnish, b. 1962). "Oil" One-liter and Four-liter Gasoline Cans. (1993). Prototype by Neste Oy, Finland.

Blow-molded polyethylene, dimensions vary.

Containment is among the most traditional roles of plastics. In Stefan Lindfors's sensuous "Oil" can, polyethylene holds gasoline. To form the vessel, air is blown into plastic, forcing its adherence to the walls of a mold. Soon to be mass-produced, this sample was made by Neste Oy in Finland.

Sanford Redmond (American, b. 1924). "dispenSRpak™" Packaging. 1987 (1986).

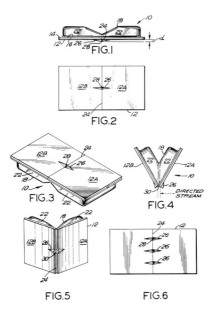

FIG.I

FIG.2

FIG.3

FIG.4

FIG.5

FIG.6

High-density polyethylene and other thermoplastics, dimensions vary.

Sanford Redmond's "dispenSRpak" (opposite), patented worldwide, can hold almost any fluid. An improvement over the innocuous, often barely functional condiment containers dispensed by fast-food restaurants, Redmond's intelligent packaging holds a broad range of liquid and viscous substances, from mayonnaise to medicinal ointments, and meets all the requirements of vacuum-seal tests and shipping. The "dispenSRpak" is produced in

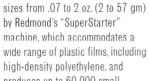

sizes from .07 to 2 oz. (2 to 57 gm) by Redmond's "SuperStarter" machine, which accommodates a wide range of plastic films, including high-density polyethylene, and produces up to 60,000 small packages per hour. With one motion of the hand, "dispenSRpak" is opened and neatly empties its contents.

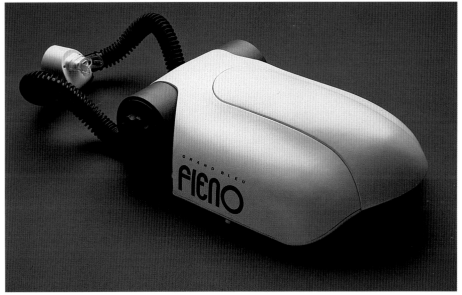

Masayuki Kurokawa (Japanese, b. 1937). "Fieno" Scuba (Self-Contained Underwater Re-breathing Apparatus). 1994 (1993). Manufactured by Grand Bleu, Inc., Japan. Injection-molded polycarbonate and polyester blend, 6 5/8 x 13 7/8 x 20 1/8" (16 x 35.2 x 51.1 cm).

The device for divers designed by Masayuki Kurokawa (above) is a technologically improved smaller and lighter interpretation of the standard scuba tank. Kurokawa's design recalls images of the gear worn by Darth Vader's guards in *Star Wars*. The "Fieno," weighing a little over 12 lbs. (5.5 kg) but essentially weightless in water, is a system housed within a polycarbonate shell. The scuba device recycles the inhaled air by funneling it through a canister containing a calcium-carbonate compound that absorbs carbon dioxide.

Even though the technology of recycling is proceeding at a very fast pace, the use of recycled compounds is not. Advancement has been thwarted by recycling's negative aesthetic image, even though there is a general awareness and interest in reprocessing waste. But the full potential of recycling has not yet effectively stimulated the imagination of the design community. The few materials here serve as examples of the compounds and products available today.

Domus Academy Research Center. "Neolite" Multipurpose Material. 1991 (1991). Manufactured by Montedipe/RPE, Italy (now Consortium Replastic, Italy).

100% heterogeneous recycled plastics, dimensions vary.

Neolite, a multipurpose material, was studied by the Domus Academy in Milan in an attempt to rid recycling of its poor image. Participants in the Domus research project included the coordinator Antonio Petrillo, and Michele Barro, Karim Azzabi, and Andrea Salas Costa; Esperanza Nuñez Castain specialized in colors and finishes; and Anna Castelli Ferrieri was a consultant. Neolite, meaning "new stone," can be extruded in lengths up to 118 in. (300 cm) and carved like wood; it can be injection-molded as well. Its textural qualities can be seen in the samples here from the first phases of production.

EnviroSafe Products. Recycled Multipurpose Materials. 1989 (1989). Manufactured by EnviroSafe Products, Inc., United States.

DuraPlast (high-density and low-density recycled plastics) and EnviroBoard (recycled plastics and wood dust), dimensions vary.

Composites, another aspect of recycling technology, illustrate the often unstyled, yet honest and appropriate, uses of waste compounds. EnviroSafe's recycled multipurpose materials (left) are produced from extruded, molded pulverized waste, adhered by resin, and manipulated, like Neolite, to produce benches, fences, and other utilitarian products.

Gino Colombini (Italian, b. 1915). Wastebaskets. 1993 (1968). Manufactured by Kartell S.p.a., Italy.

100% recycled plastics, dimensions vary.

These wastebaskets produced by Kartell are made from recycled plastics and based on a classical design by Gino Colombini, the designer of many domestic objects manufactured by Kartell in the 1950s and 1960s.

David Hertz (American, b. 1960). "Syndecrete®" Composite Material. 1984 (1984). Manufactured by Syndesis, Inc., United States.

Cement-based composite of recycled materials, dimensions vary.

Syndecrete is a cement-based compound that demonstrates excellent plasticity. Already well known to the design community, it behaves like a very hard wood that can be sawed. A mixture of a fine volcanic aggregate, it is usually integrally pigmented, precast in molds, and handground, sealed, and waxed. This produces a decorative, smooth terrazzo-type material. Syndecrete is available in finished form only, not as a powder, and maintained as if it were fine stone. It accepts plastic shavings and pieces of glass or steel, and it has in the past included what appears to be an endless variety of additives—even nails, metal chain, acorns, pencils, golf tees, wood chips, and computer chips.

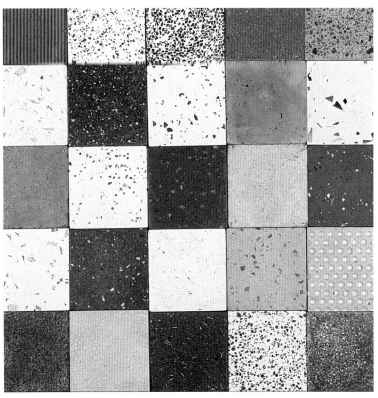

Christopher Connell (Australian, b. 1954) of MAP International. "Plaky" Table. 1993 (1992). Manufactured by MAP (Merchants of Australian Products Pty., Ltd.), Australia. Recycled ABS-polycarbonate blend top and anodized-aluminum pedestal, 28 3/8 h. x 23 5/8" dia. (72 h. x 60 cm dia.).

The "Plaky" table represents a mature example of a recycled plastic product, as do Gaetano Pesce's armchair and stools (opposite). The table, designed and produced in Australia by Christopher Connell, employs a recycled blend of ABS and a polycarbonate. The compound is re-extruded, granulated, and cast again in a mold in which the behavior of the two different materials creates an odd, confettilike surface effect.

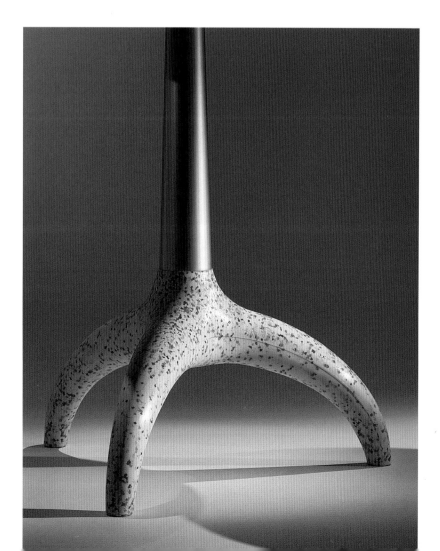

Gaetano Pesce (Italian, b. 1939). "Seaweed" Chair. 1991 (1991). Manufactured by Pesce, Ltd., United States. Resin-impregnated shredded fabrics, 32 x 45 x 31" (81.3 x 114.3 x 78.7 cm).

Pesce's armchair and stools are made of strips of waste fabrics bathed in resin. The stools, formed with a higher density of resin than the chair, hide the surprise of sound. When kicked, they moo like a cow or ring like a bell. Each armchair or stool is the result of the serendipitous distribution of colors and materials.

Gaetano Pesce (Italian, b. 1939). Low Stools or Ottomans. 1994 (1994). Manufactured by Pesce, Ltd., United States. Resin-impregnated shredded fabrics, 17 x 18 x 15" (43.2 x 45.7 x 38.1 cm).

Ceramics are considered by many the materials of the future. Ceramic automobile engines will waste little energy and require no lubricants, superconducting ceramics will transmit energy without wasting it, and ceramic fibers will protect the human body from changing temperatures and bullets.

"Traditional ceramics can be very soft and almost flow," says Eva Zeisel, whose sensual organic shapes have given life to ceramics in the decorative arts for over fifty years. "My ceramic objects are all made to be touchable." But advanced ceramics, a development of the last few decades, are often far from being touchable. They differ from traditional ceramics in their composition, which includes quantities of metallic powders, such as alumina, titania, sand, feldspar, and the rare earth powders yttria and zirconia.

Clay firing existed for millennia as a process for making objects, almost as instinctive as the preparation of food: earth powders mixed with water, then shaped and baked at high temperatures. Ceramic production has also borrowed many of the processes used for forming metals, such as sintering, which transforms powders into solids at extremely high temperatures and has utilized some of the techniques for making glass, with which ceramics are often even physically coupled.

Slip casting is the most traditional ceramic technology and is still used in the production of many domestic objects, like Lisa Krohn and Aaron Lown's condom keeper (page 50). In this process liquid clay, known as slip, is poured into porous molds that absorb its water content. Today, the powders are mixed with a special solvent before being cast, and the mold absorbs and eliminates the solvent in the process. Wax molds are used to produce more complex shapes like those of turbine rotors (page 46). Newer technologies can achieve more isotropic, robust materials that are usually machined to a final shape after molding.

Ceramic injection molding uses a support polymer, which is melted away by the temperature of the furnace; a similar method was also used to produce the ceramic foam for the lamps by Harry Allen (pages 48 and 49). Hot isostatic pressing is a fascinating yet extremely complex technology in which an envelope of heat-resistant glass is wrapped around the ceramic object and then exposed to gas heat and pressure.

Advanced ceramics, along with plastics and composites, will have an impact on our material culture similar to that of reinforced concrete and steel frames on our built environment. Through the work of chemical engineers, new molecular support systems are changing the inner architecture of materials, making them more efficient and stable.

Eva Zeisel. "Museum" Dinnerware. 1946 (1941). Porcelain, various dimensions. Manufactured by Castleton China, Inc., United States.

Ceramics

Like plastics, the variety and nature of ceramics are wide-ranging. To produce a ceramic, ordinary and rare powders are mixed into a viscous mass, formed into objects, and usually heated at high temperatures, which stabilizes and makes them permanent. A delicate porcelain teacup and sturdy industrial turbine rotor are inherently the same. Yet, advanced ceramics are very special mutants. With the characteristics of traditional ceramics, including chemical inertness, advanced ceramics have enhanced hardness, heat resistance, nonconductivity, and abrasion resistance. Second only to diamonds in hardness, advanced ceramics have the appearance of smooth, plasticlike metals. They are imbued with physical stability and structural resistance and can be produced in highly precise shapes, capable even of supplanting metal in the production of shaving blades. A disadvantage is that this high-tech material will chip when it strikes a hard surface or is dropped.

Fine Ceramics Division of Kyocera Corporation. Turbine Rotor. (1992). Prototype by Kyocera Corporation, Japan.

Silicon nitride, 4 h. x 10" dia. (10.2 h. x 25.4 cm dia.).

The use of a ceramic compound of silicon and nitrogen in turbo-supercharger rotors (below) reduces both mass and inertia, diminishing "turbo lag" in automotive engines. Ceramic engine parts are able to function at much higher temperatures than those of other materials and typically require no lubricant.

Fine Ceramics Division of Kyocera Corporation. Automotive Engine Components. 1992 (1992). Manufactured by Kyocera Corporation, Japan.

Silicon nitride, dimensions vary.

These ceramic automotive engine components can reduce pollution significantly by allowing higher operating temperatures and fuel pressures than those in conventional engines.

3M Unitek. "Transcend Series 6000" Tooth Brackets. 1987 (1986). Manufactured by 3M Unitek/3M Dental Products Division, United States.

TPA (translucent-polycrystalline-alumina), $5/32$ x $5/32$ x $1/8$" (.4 x .4 x .3 cm).

Ceramics relating to the human body are another interesting application of these technologically advanced materials. The biological inertness of a ceramic makes it ideal for artificial implants—from prosthetic joints and bones to false teeth and braces for the teeth. The braces (right) by 3M Unitek used in orthodontics are made of TPA. The process involves pressing powdered alumina (aluminum oxide) into a bracket-shaped die and sintering (high-firing without melting). The bracket form is machined as the last step before it is ready to be attached to the tooth by an orthodontic adhesive. Usually a shape-memory alloy wire is inserted in the bracket-arch wire slot to facilitate movement of the teeth.

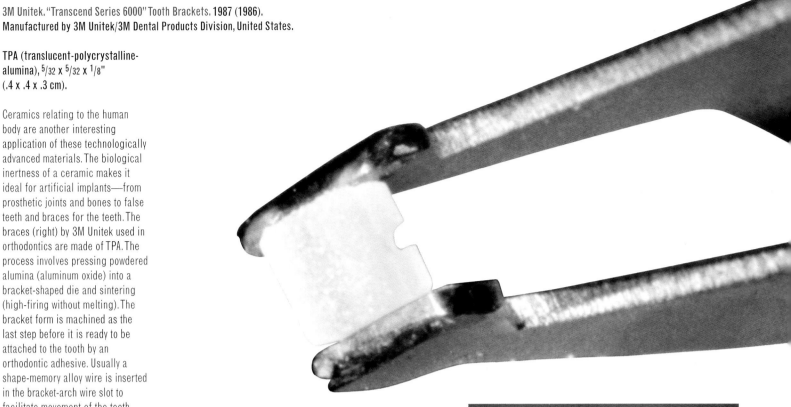

CERATIP Cutting Tool Division of Kyocera Industrial Ceramics Corporation. Cutting Tools. 1992 (1992). Manufactured by Kyocera Industrial Ceramics Corporation, United States.

Aluminum-oxide- and titanium-carbide-coated ceramic and Cermet (a ceramic-metal composite), dimensions vary.

The precision made possible by ceramics is illustrated by the Cermet cutting tool, made of titanium carbonitrides with metal carbides. Cermet features a uniform super-fine microstructure that results in extreme hardness and toughness. Compared to conventional metallic cutting tools, Cermet tools cut at higher speeds with reduced heat, hold a cutting edge longer, and maintain an excellent surface finish.

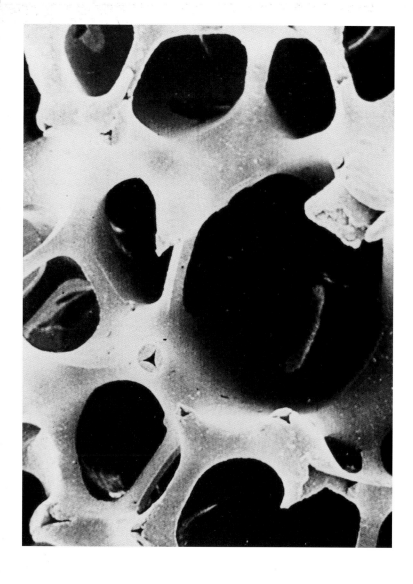

Harry Allen (American, b. 1964). Lighting Fixtures. 1994 (1994).
Manufactured by Harry Allen and Associates, United States.

Ceramic foam, three sizes:
33 h. x 6" dia. (84 h. x 15.2 cm dia.),
54 h. x 8" dia. (137.2 h. x 20.3 cm dia.),
and 74 h. x 10" dia.
(188 h. x 25.4 cm dia.).

Ceramics are known for their capacity to be formed as substantial objects, but they can also be made in a spongelike material. Harry Allen has designed a series of lighting fixtures in which this mutant material is used. He chose ceramic foam for its expressive, as well as practical, qualities. Ceramic foam is the material normally used in the construction of kiln equipment, ferrous and nonferrous metal filtration systems, automotive-emissions control devices, biotechnical applications, and petrochemical production. Selee® ceramic foam, a curious group of materials manufactured since the early 1970s, is produced by impregnating open-cell polyurethane foam with various oxides that range from pure alumina to compounds including yttrium and zirconium. Allen chose Selee A, containing only aluminum oxide. The impregnated compound is fired in a precision high-temperature furnace where the polyurethane is burned away, leaving a finished substance with the appearance of deep-sea coral. Different foam shapes, in various densities expressed in inch ratios, are created by drilling, machining, or both.

Werner Scholpp (German, b. 1946) of Scholpp Produktgestaltung.
"DiaStar Ceramica"Wrist Watch. 1989 (1986).
Manufactured by RADO Watch Co., Ltd., Switzerland.

Zircon-Y ceramic case, bracelet,
and crown; sapphire crystal; and
stainless-steel back plate and
safety clasp; dimensions vary.

The "Ceramica" watch (right) takes
advantage of high-tech ceramics'
most distinctive qualities:
resistance to abrasion and an
exceptionally smooth texture. The
band, case, and crown are made of
the ceramic material known as
zircon-Y. The individual ceramic
components are sintered, shaped
with diamond-tipped tools, and
assembled with steel framework.
Stainless steel is used for the
safety clasp. In the final assembly
of the case, the sapphire crystal is
glued at low temperature to the
ceramic case, and the timepiece is
made watertight by a steel plate
sealed under pressure.

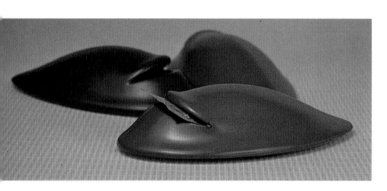

Lisa Krohn (American, b. 1963) and Aaron Lown (American, b. 1968).
"Safe" Condom Keeper. (1992). Prototype.

Porcelain, 2 x 3 7/8 x 7 1/2"
(5.1 x 9.9 x 19.1 cm).

Traditional ceramic materials and
technologies, used for millennia for
decorative objects and utilitarian
containers, were chosen to produce
an ingenious contemporary object.
Lisa Krohn and Aaron Lown's
"Safe" condom keeper (above) is
created by slip-casting. The
process involves the pouring of
liquid clay into a plaster mold,
draining it after a short time,
drying, and kiln-firing at a high
temperature, after which it is
glazed and fired again at a lower
temperature. A strip of three
condoms can be removed from the
opening of the keeper as easily as
tissues from a box.

Ross Lovegrove (British, b. 1958) of Studio X. "Advanced Wet Shave" Razor. (1993). Prototype by M.L. Laboratories, Great Britain. Zircon-Y blade and injection-molded acrylic handle, 3 3/16 x 13/16" (8 x 2.2 cm).

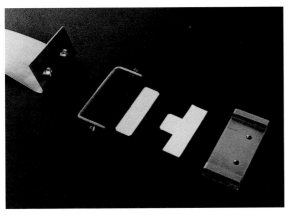

Whether formed into dental braces or razor blades, an advanced ceramic will chip when dropped or abruptly struck, because the grain structure maintains the original rigid form. Even so, its attributes far outweigh its disadvantages. An advanced ceramic's resistance to rust or corrosion and ability to take an extraordinarily sharp edge made it a rational choice for Ross Lovegrove's shaving razor. The injection-molded acrylic handle of the razor may wear out long before the blade. Illustrated (left) in a material that will not be used in the final production, the razor's small head incorporates a zircon-Y ceramic blade that can be removed along with the head and replaced should the blade become chipped. The supersharp blade is coated with a micro-thin layer of titanium. The prototype (above) includes a high-alumina-content ceramic blade with a single-honed edge. The edge of zircon-Y blades on the eventual production version will be double-ground and removable.

The lightness and resistance of composite materials is well represented by Takeshi Ishiguro's lighting fixture—a sleek, calligraphic structure topped by a feather (page 54). The strong, light, and fluid shapes made possible by carbon fibers are advantageous in the manufacture of boats, chairs, tennis rackets, and airplanes. According to Burt Rutan, a pioneer in the application of composites in the aerospace industry, "Since the introduction of composites, structures look considerably different today. They appear very plastic, yet they are not built of plastics but rather of an extremely strong high-fiber-content material."

The idea of a composite material is not new. Huts made of mud and straw are precursors of carbon-fiber applications. In contemporary composites, thermosetting resins, like epoxy or polyethylene, are the surrogates for mud and the aramid, carbon, or glass fibers the replacement for straw.

There are two main types of composite materials. The most common includes reinforced fibers embedded in a thermosetting resin matrix. According to Rutan, "The careful and intelligent planning of fiber placement is the basic method for improving composites." The fibers are laid in the matrix according to the strain they will bear and can be spun to create an isotropic material, oriented in one or two directions or superimposed in layers. The soft sheet is formed, either in a mold or partially hand-sculpted, and cured by heat. The technology is illustrated by the knee braces and in-line skate boots on page 58, among other objects.

The other principal type of composite material is a sandwich of thin sheets separated by an inner core, most commonly of a porous yet rigid material, such as an aluminum or synthetic honeycomb, or a foam. The outer layers are usually sheets of carbon fibers, fiberglass, or even wood. Eric Goetz's fiber-based materials (page 59) illustrate the use of wood as an element in composites.

The possibilities of creating composites with numerous layers and materials with individual characteristics are vast and await further development. Some technologies, like pultrusion—exploited in the structural sections of bridges shown on page 66—require high-cost tooling, while others invite hands-on experimentation and craft techniques. Professional and lay engineers exchange technological recipes. These technology-transfer dialogues and other aspects of experimentation have contributed to making the field of composites the most lively in the universe of materials.

Fibers and Composites

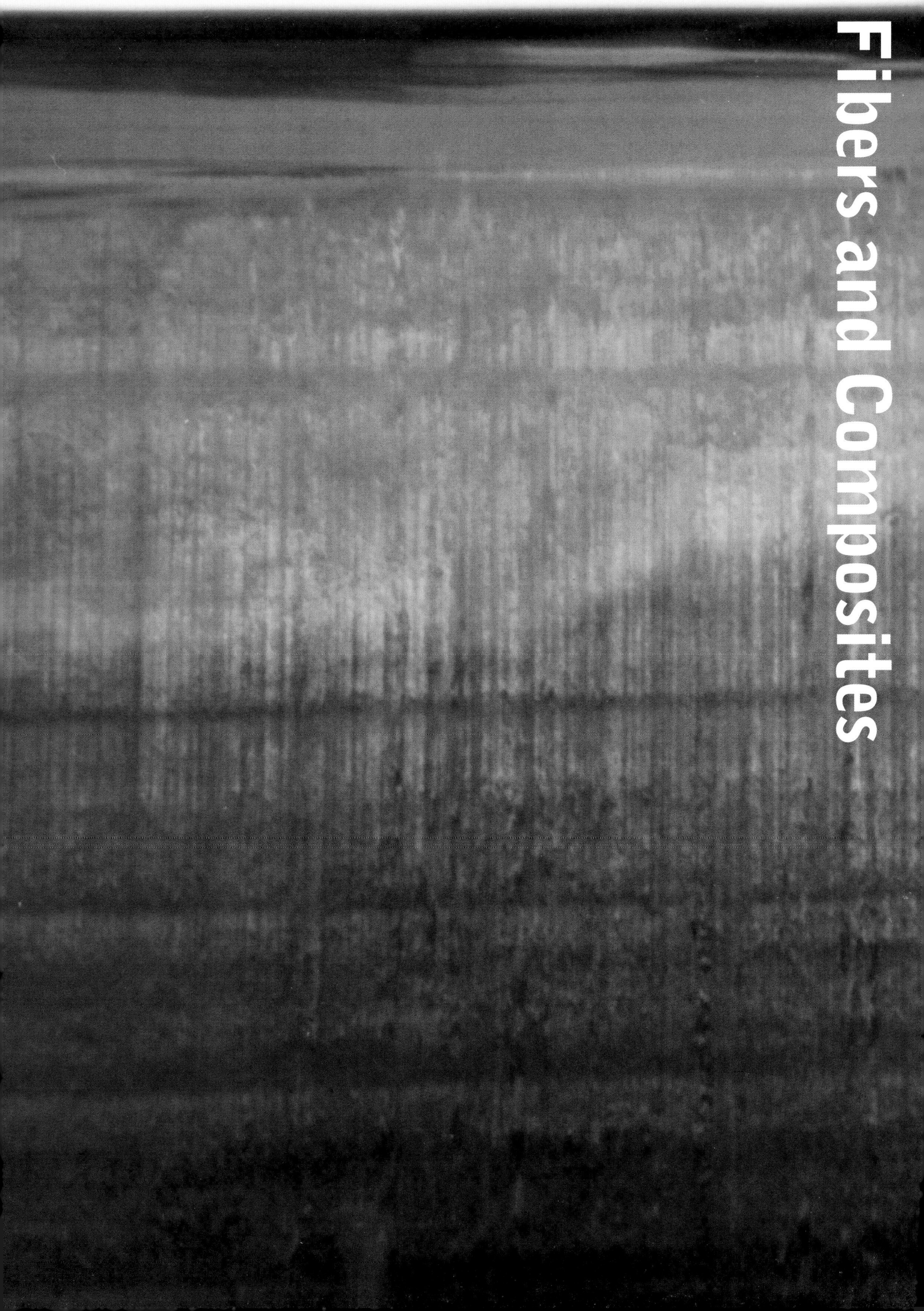

Takeshi Ishiguro (Japanese, b. 1969). "Light Light" Lighting Fixture. (1994). Prototype. Carbon fiber body, cast-aluminum pedestal, slip-cast porcelain bottom reflector, and bird's feather upper reflector; 19 1/2 x 4 x 19 1/2" (80 x 10 x 80 cm).

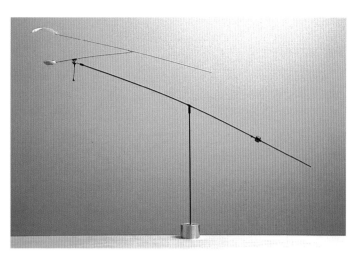

While a student at London's Royal College of Art, Takeshi Ishiguro designed the bedroom fixture "Light Light" to serve as, in his words, "a dreamy object . . . an object of contemplation as well as illumination." To make it as lightweight as possible, he built the undulating lamp with carbon fiber; a counterweight balances the lithely dancing limbs. The bottom reflector was made of slip-cast porcelain in the shape of a fragile egg—a symbol of simplicity. The top reflector, a real bird's feather, was chosen as a metaphor for the structure's weightless nature, according to the designer, "because I could not find a better material."

Shozo Toyohisa (Japanese, b. 1960) of Super Lattice/Kilt Planning Office.
"Mylight" Lighting System. 1994 (1994).
Manufactured by Asahi Glass Co., Ltd., Japan.

Flexible glass-core optical fiber
and 150-watt metal-halide light
bulb, dimensions vary.

One of the numerous applications possible with plastic optical-fiber lighting technology, Shozo Toyohisa's system (right and below) was developed in Japan. Its quartz-core optical fiber has better thermal resistance and higher maximum light intensity than traditional plastic optical fibers. Both of these features have contributed to a superior lighting fixture that is stronger than optical-fiber lighting of the past and can be installed not only under water but also in other hard-to-maintain places, such as museum cases and underground tunnels. Since quartz is used as the core material in Toyohisa's system, only one high-powered metal-halide source is necessary to power a ten-branch polymer-clad optical silica fiber. Each fixture emits the equivalent of 35 halogen watts. The four different heads, serving as diffusers or reflectors, can be attached to a single branch.

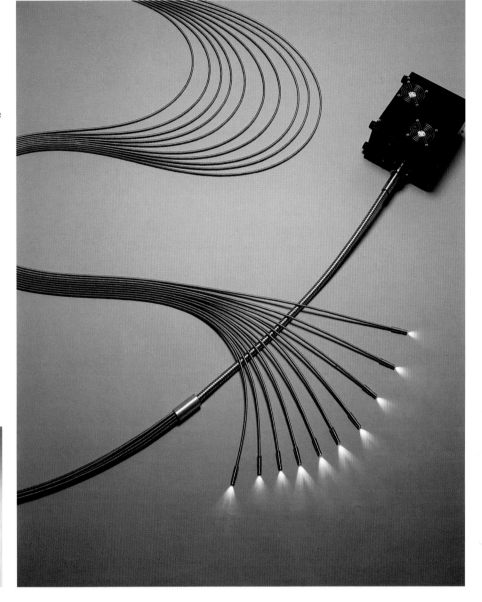

William Hudson (American, b. 1958), Angela Kortelink (Dutch, b. 1959), and Siamak Samii (Iranian, b. 1958). "Bilange" Body Sponge. 1989 (1988). Manufactured by Bilange, Inc., United States.

Netted extruded-polyethylene
fiber, 4 1/2" (11.4 cm) dia. The
Museum of Modern Art, New York,
gift of the manufacturer.

A soft, airy sponge made of nonporous netting, the "Bilange" sponge (right) is almost entirely handmade. Precolored polyethylene is extruded into a netted filament that is handstretched into the final fluffy form—a "puff" that has no absorption characteristics. The brightly colored material is far more inviting to the touch than other scrubbing defoliants, such as loofahs or hemp-woven mitts, and, unlike them, resists mildew and bacteria.

Donald Chadwick (American, b. 1936) and William Stumpf (American, b. 1936). "Aeron" Office Chair. 1994 (1992). Manufactured by Herman Miller, Inc., United States.

Die-cast glass-reinforced polyester, aluminum, Hytrel® polymer, polyester, and Lycra®; 43 1/2 x 27 x 19" (110.5 x 68.6 x 48.3 cm). The Museum of Modern Art, New York, gift of the employees of Herman Miller.

The "Aeron" office chair, in sports and automotive jargon, is a high-performance object. Its aesthetics celebrate the power of technology; its comfort is exceptional. The body rests on little more than a fiber net supported by a skeletal frame "like a Thonet chair," the inspiration acknowledged by codesigner Donald Chadwick. The Pellicle™ mesh fabric is woven using a polyester elastomer from Du Pont, originally used as an inner support material for car seats. It relieves sitter strain by changing its shape and responding only in localized areas. Once the sitter stands up, the fiber's almost perfect elastic memory cancels the deformation. The highly articulable chair features seat-height adjustment in a much wider range than other chairs; it can be made to recline for relaxation or incline to accommodate those, for example, who work with microscopes. The tilt action can be regulated to varying degrees of tautness. The armrests can be swung into different stationary positions depending on worker tasks, converging for computer keyboard operation or diverging for more restful repose. The "Aeron" is available in three sizes, in deference to body-size variety.

frogdesign. "Ultratech" Orthopedic Knee Braces. 1992 (1991).
Manufactured by Biedermann Motech GmbH, Germany.

Injection-molded and pressed ATP
(adenosine triphosphate) carbon-
fiber composites, neoprene
padding, titanium and aluminum
hinges, and steel bolts;
17 5/16 x 5 1/2 x 7 1/2"
(44 x 14 x 19 cm).

Sharing Chadwick and Stumpf's
"Aeron" hyperorganic, mechanistic
aesthetic but in a different material,
frogdesign's knee braces (right)
are for people who have had knee-
ligament injuries. Worn like a ski
boot, the brace offers freedom of
motion and, after an accident or
surgery, facilitates physical exercise
in order to rebuild muscle tissue
and prevent knee stiffening. The
molded carbon-fiber version is
custom-made from a plaster
model of the individual limb. The
standard-model Ultratech brace in
injection-molded Durethan-B®
polyamide, like the carbon-fiber
custom version, is fitted with neoprene
inserts to soften the grip on the
leg. The thinness of the .078 in.
(2 mm) carbon fiber makes the
brace undetectable under clothing.

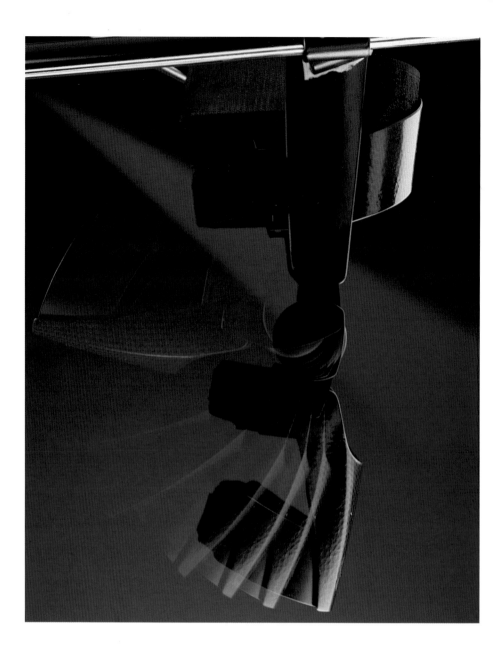

Scott Riegelman (American, b. 1957). In-line Skate Boots. 1994 (1994).
Inner shell manufactured by BioMechanical Composites, United States,
for Riedell Skating Shoes, Inc., United States.

Molded acrylic-resin-impregnated
carbon-graphite inner shell and
other materials, dimensions vary.

Riedell's racing skates (above) are
fitted with an inner shell (left) that
conforms to the human foot.
BioMechanical Composites'
proprietary thermoplastic lay-up
process produces the shell by
forming a toughened acrylic-resin-
impregnated graphite fabric over a
mold. The technique makes the
fabrication of complex shapes
possible and permits the placement
of directional fibers in certain
high-stress areas of the
components. The shell can be
adjusted by heat for a custom fit.

David Schwartz (American, b. 1948). Sailboat Mast Sections. 1994 (1994). Manufactured by Goetz Marine Technologies (GMT), Inc., United States.

Heat- and pressure-cured carbon fiber and pre-impregnated carbon laminate, dimensions vary.

Plasticity is one of the many desirable properties of fiber composites. Able to assume infinite shapes, objects formed from fiber composites have become the lightweight alternative to heavier materials, such as metals—particularly aluminum—in the construction of sailboat masts. Even though aluminum is durable and reliable, carbon composites are lighter and easier to treat and customize. Goetz Marine Technologies built its first carbon masts in 1989 and has been testing their virtues in international sailing competitions, like the BOC and the America's Cup. Carbon-fiber masts have proved to be more impervious to salt water than aluminum. And, important to racing-boat construction, fiber masts are lighter. The two mast sections (right) are fitted to 40 to 50 ft. (12.3 to 21.5 m) boats. The vertical example, painted with a white finish, allows the mainsail to be furled within. Had these 60 ft. masts been built of aluminum, they would each weigh 250 lbs. (127.8 kg), rather than 120 lbs. (54.5 kg) in laminated carbon fiber.

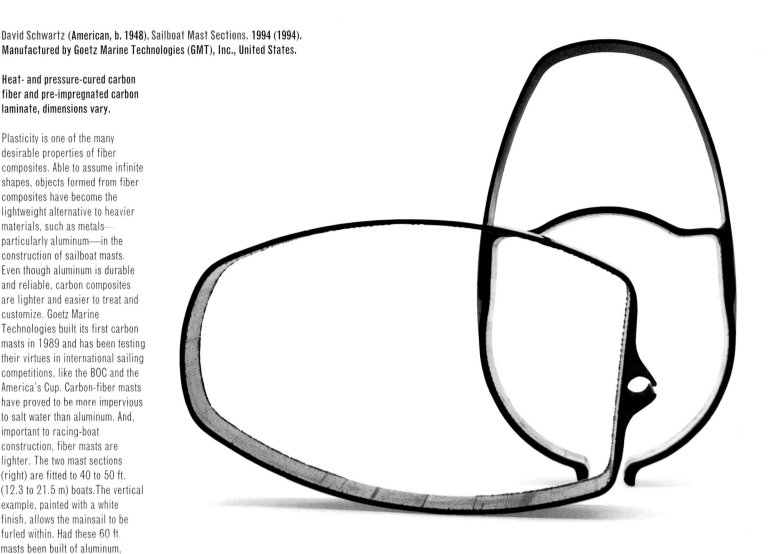

Eric Goetz (American b. 1949). Samples of Composite Fiber-based Materials. 1994 (1994). Manufactured by Eric Goetz Custom Sailboats, Inc., United States.

Molded carbon fiber in an epoxy-resin matrix, aramid (aromatic-polyamide) fibers, mahogany-laminated plywood, aluminum honeycomb, and stainless steel; various dimensions.

Emphasizing the alchemical nature of the design of materials, most of these composite examples are used in the marine industry. The early composite for the deck of the 1983 52 ft. (16 m) sailboat, the *Golden Eagle*, was made of mahogany-plywood skins with a Nomex® honeycomb core bonded with epoxy resin (bottom). The example of a contemporary composite (middle) from the 1994 America's Cup racer, the *America³*, was built with an aluminum-honeycomb core and carbon-fiber skins treated with "prepreg" technology, in which carbon or Kevlar® fabric is impregnated by an outside supplier, shipped in dry ice, and kept frozen so that the epoxy remains in an uncured, soft state. The material is applied to the mold and then cured at a temperature of 203° F. (95° C.). The weight is controlled by regulating resin quantities. The toggle (upper left), cut from a carbon chainplate, which attaches the mast to a boat, was manufactured for the Maxi racer, *Matador²*. The carbon fabric was hand-laid around a stainless-steel ferrule. The chainplate withstands loads in excess of 100,000 lbs. (45,500 kg). For applications other than the marine industry, a curved panel of thin carbon skins over a balsa-wood core (upper right) is used in the production of furniture; the core adds stiffness to the carbon skins, and the clear coating allows the grain of the carbon to show through.

William Masters (American, b. 1950), Allen Stancil (American, b. 1951), and Gary Barton (British, b. 1958). "Sea Lion" Kayak. 1994 (1987). Manufactured by Upstream Edge/Rockwood Outfitters, Canada, for Perception, Inc., United States.

Molded carbon fiber, Kevlar®, S-glass, and Spheretex® in an epoxy-resin matrix; 13 1/2 x 22 x 204" (34.3 x 55.9 x 518.2 cm).

Technologically advanced composites—lightweight, durable, reliable, and easy to customize— serve as an alternative to other thermoplastics used in recreational sports equipment, including sea kayaks, which are shaped differently from fresh-water versions. The exterior shell of the "Sea Lion" kayak is formed by spraying polished molds with color-impregnated resin; all visual design elements are applied at this stage. After drying, epoxy resin and layers of S-glass, Kevlar, carbon fiber, and Spheretex (a special lightweight, woven fiberglass) are laid on. The resin is then sealed in a vacuum bag and heat-cured overnight. The parts are removed from the molds, and excess flashing is trimmed. The deck and hull, created in separate molds, are seamed inside and out using fiberglass and epoxy resin. A series of fittings follows. Rims in three openings (the cockpit and two storage hatches) are installed. The foot braces, rudder, seat, and deck rigging are attached. The two storage hatches are fitted with neoprene covers that keep out water and rigid fiberglass lids that match the boat's outer-shell color. Finally, the backrest, made of a sewn-and-stitched nylon fabric with a foam-padding insert, is put in place.

Lance Neibauer (American, b. 1949). "Lancair 320 MKII" Airplane. 1988 (1987). Manufactured by Lancair International, Inc., United States. Molded carbon fiber and E-glass in an epoxy-resin matrix, 252 x 282" (640 x 716 cm).

New technology based on composite sandwich structures has revolutionized the world of aviation, particularly in the construction of small, light aircraft. In many cases kit-built airplanes have led the way in the application of these materials. The "Lancair 320" is sleek, elegant, and, according to experts, among the best in the field. Priced at an affordable $45,000 in kit form, its assembly purportedly requires up to 1,500 hours. The airframe is fabricated to aerospace standards using high-temperature epoxy, "prepreg" carbon fiber, and E-glass fibers. Core materials are Du Pont's Nomex® honeycomb, known for its high strength, light weight, and outstanding thermal stability. All materials are tested and analyzed under various conditions, both at room temperature and in the "hot/wet" condition, with full humidity saturation.

Alberto Meda (Italian, b. 1945). "Light Light" Chair. 1987 (1987). Manufactured by Alias S.r.l., Italy. Molded carbon fiber in an epoxy-resin matrix and Nomex® honeycomb, 29 1/4 x 15 x 19 1/2" (74.3 x 38.3 x 49.5 cm). The Museum of Modern Art, New York, gift of the manufacturer.

Alberto Meda began his professional career in engineering in 1970. His knowledge of advanced technology has been applied to the reinvention of traditional objects, such as chairs, which in his hands become light, sleek, and minimal through the use of unconventional materials. Meda's "Light Light" (left) and "SoftLight" (opposite) chairs continue the universal search for lightness in furniture initiated by other designers, such as Gio Ponti and his "Superleggera" chair of 1952, and encourage people, who have been holding onto traditional materials, to adapt to the use of new ones. "Light Light," Meda's first lightweight chair, was built with a Nomex-honeycomb core, and the surface is a carbon fiber embedded in epoxy resin; it weighs only about 2 lbs. (1 kg). The direction of the fiber is strategically placed on areas of the chair to counteract the force transmitted by the weight of the sitter. Additional unidirectional fibers are applied to reinforce the joints, where stress is greatest. A limited number of "Light Light" chairs were made, but the "SoftLight"—also in carbon fiber but with the inner honeycomb in aluminum—is mass produced. The seat and back of "SoftLight" are of Dymetrol elastic fabric, whose warp is polyester and weft is an elastomeric filament. Dymetrol, a Du Pont product, is yet another high-performance material originally developed for the automotive industry.

Alberto Meda (Italian, b.1945). "SoftLight" Chair. 1989 (1988). Molded carbon fiber in an epoxy-resin matrix, aluminum honeycomb, and Dymetrol® elastic fiber; 28 x 20 3/4 x 16 1/2" (71.3 x 52.7 x 42 cm). The Museum of Modern Art, New York, gift of the manufacturer.

Richard Sapper (German, b. 1932) and Samuel Lucente (American, b. 1958) of IBM Corporate Strategic Design. "Leapfrog" Computer. 1993 (1989). Manufactured by IBM Corporation, United States.

Carbon-fiber reinforced-plastic top cover, magnesium-alloy bottom cover, ABS keyboard housing, and other materials; 10 13/16 x 1 3/16 x 13 11/16" (27.5 x 3 x 34.8 cm).

The experimental "Leapfrog" was done in coordination with the IBM Research & Development teams of Hawthorne, New York; Raleigh, North Carolina; and Yamamoto, Japan. This limited-production computer features a pen-based color tablet, which can be rotated in both vertical and horizontal positions, and a keyboard with an integrated pointing device. In addition, it accommodates handwriting- and voice-recognition technologies. As a desktop workstation, the base provides keyboard storage and ports for the diskette drive and for standard desktop peripherals. The lightweight 1 9/32 in. (3 cm) thick tablet contains a powerful 486 processor, hard-disk drive, thin-film-transistor (TFT) display, digitizer, digital-signal processor, batteries (if used), a slot for two PC (personal computer) cards, and receptacles for a headphone and microphone. The surface of the color screen, level with the top cover, is textured to simulate the sensation of lead pencil on paper. Recessed controls and light indicators are located on the face. Offset internal components create an asymmetrical palmrest for a right- or left-handed user. Fold-down legs support the unit. In 1991, a complex volumetric maquette of the "Leapfrog" tablet (opposite) was made up using an "integrated packaging design" concept. To achieve economy of design, thin-wall composite

materials with integrated three-dimensional circuitry for the electrical connections were specified. The components were color-coded by function and configured to eliminate cables from the assembly, to reduce weight, volume, and the number of parts, and to provide increased reliability and performance by lessening the number of interconnections and cables. Thin-walled 1/32 in. (2 mm) carbon-fiber reinforced plastic, used to form the "Leapfrog" tablet top cover, eliminates the necessity for intricate component-mounting design features. The nonflammable material offers increased strength, reduces weight, heightens the modulus, and increases the electromagnetic-interference (EMI) shielding. In the manufacturing process, 1 in. (2.5 cm) long, random-chopped carbon fiber was impregnated with a phenol-resin composition. The material was molded by compression for sixty seconds at 300–400° F. (150°– 200° C.), cooled, removed from the form, and then coated with a "soft finish" plastic paint. The painted finish lends a pleasing hand and texture to the case. The "Leapfrog" bottom cover was made from rigid heat-dissipating 1/64 in. (1 mm) magnesium. The tilting stand-base was produced from a special vacuum-cast mold using polycarbonate plastics. The keyboard housing was fabricated from injection blow-molded ABS.

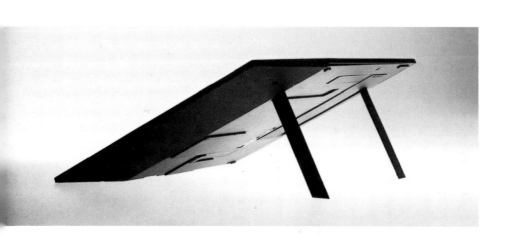

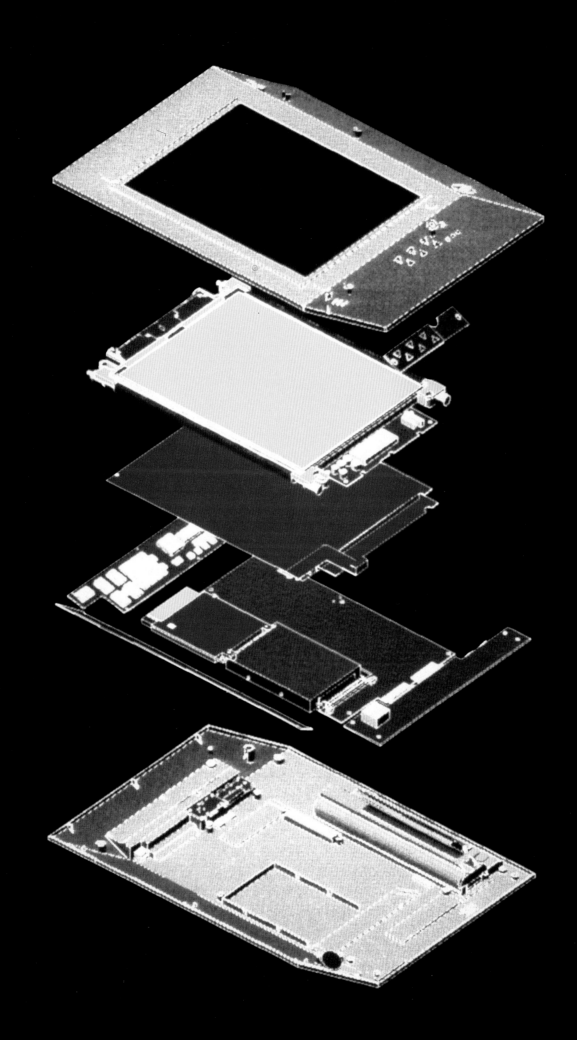

Maunsell Structural, Plastics Ltd,. of International Consulting Civil and Structural Engineers, Maunsell Group. "ACCS" (Advanced Composite Construction System). 1987 (1982). Manufactured by Designer Composites Technology, Ltd., Great Britain.

Modular system of glass-reinforced polyester pultrusions, dimensions vary.

The fiberglass-reinforced-plastic "ACCS" (below), invented by Maunsell Structural Plastics in 1982, is a versatile, advanced modular construction system, which combines automated production with structural and fire-retardancy performance. In the manufacture of the "ACCS," a polyester-resin binder holds the glass reinforcement in position, giving the material its rigidity. The manufacturing process for producing continuous lengths of reinforced structural-plastic shapes is known as pultrusion.
The raw materials used to make advanced composites are flexible, reinforcing textile fibers and a liquid-resin mixture, containing a filler and special additives. Rather than being pushed through, as in the extrusion process, the resin mix and textile fibers are pulled through a heated steel form (die) using a continuous pulling device. The reinforcement material is saturated with the resin mixture in a resin bath and pulled through the die, where further resin may be injected. The resin is cured by heat, and a rigid profile is formed in the shape of the die. A caterpillar-type mechanism pulls the composite out of the die, and it is finally cut to size by a flying saw.

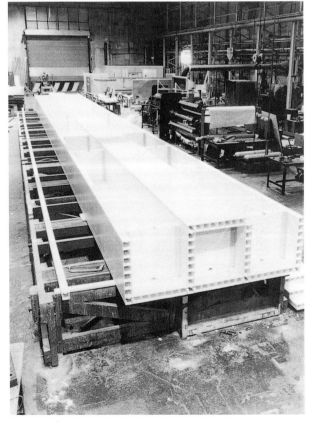

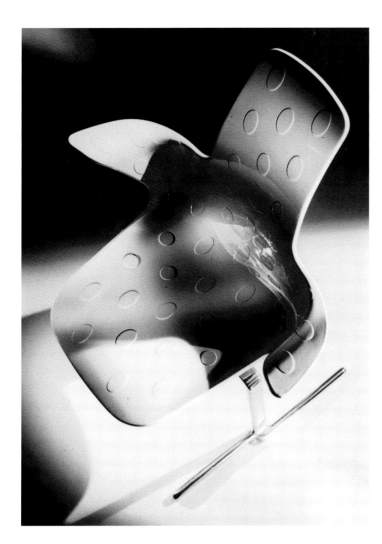

Stefan Lindfors (Finnish, b. 1962). "Kemper Museum Chair." 1994 (1994). Manufactured by the Kansas City Art Institute, Kansas City, Missouri.

Double-molded gel-coated fiberglass and polished sand-cast aluminum, 34 x 25 1/2 x 17" (86.5 x 65 x 43.5 cm).

The "Kemper Museum Chair" is produced in fiberglass by a double-mold process which eliminates exposed fibers of the type that appeared on furniture of the 1950s, such as the Charles and Ray Eames chairs. The organic quality of the undulating surface and disk shapes suggests the hand's role in the deformation of the chair. The seat is bright-white gel-coated fiberglass, and the legs are polished sand-cast aluminum. Commissioned by R. Crosby Kemper for The Kemper Museum of Contemporary Art and Design, Stefan Lindfors's furniture collection consists of benches for the museum's galleries and chairs, tables, and a maître d' station for its café. The materials were selected for their compatibility with the clean lines of the building designed by architect Gunnar Birkerts.

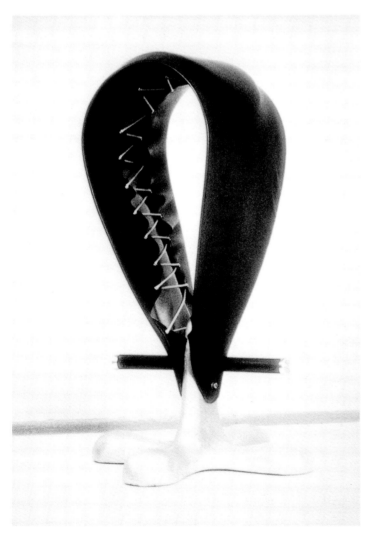

Aaron Lown (American, b. 1968) of C4 Design Laboratories. "Hi Ho" Stool. (1994). Prototype.

Fiberglass, urethane foam, aluminum, and leather; 28 1/2 x 17 1/2 x 17 1/2" (72.4 x 43.2 x 43.2 cm).

Fiberglass is used in conjunction with aluminum and leather in Aaron Lown's stool. For his prototype, multiple layers of fiberglass were laminated together using a vacuum press. These were laid over a solid form that was placed in an airtight plastic bag. Air was removed from the bag by a vacuum pump, which creates even pressure against the form. The finished form was then slipped into a leather sheath and laced on the interior. Traditional sand casting was used to form the metal base. In this process, a special mixture of sand and resin is packed around a wood form. This positive shape is then removed, leaving a cavity that receives the molten aluminum. Machined aluminum foot pegs are used to fasten the stool together.

A separate section on objects that are flexible and soft might seem arbitrary from a scientific viewpoint, since most of these soft objects are made of synthetic polymers. Their uniqueness and diversity warrant a category of their own, even though they are plastics. "There are probably as many plastics as there are cheeses," suggests Stephen Peart, whose wet suit appears here and on pages 82 and 83.

The development of thermoplastic elastomers (TPEs) has been an important recent breakthrough. According to Peart, "A decade or so ago, you couldn't get injection-moldable raw materials that come out soft." Even though thermoplastic polyurethane has been available since the 1950s and many TPEs since the 1970s, advanced materials were not always as easily accessible to designers as they are today. Now communications networks have been organized among designers, and manufacturers have begun to seek designers' interpretations of engineered materials.

TPEs can have the characteristics of natural rubbers. They can also be formed in a more economical, varied manner using thermoplastic technologies such as injection and blow molding. The TPE known as Santoprene® was used to form the molded details of textural reliefs and complex shapes of the objects on pages 80 and 81. Peart and Ross Lovegrove took advantage of polyurethane foam, originally developed by the aerospace industry, for the production of their lumbar support (page 78). Temporarily formed by body heat, the material can remember the shape. While its flow quality is good, its performance is exceeded by other open-cell foams, such as the padding developed by NASA (also page 78).

The polyurethane family appears to be an endless source of innovation and application, but also, at times, of disillusionment. Cini Boeri's "Serpentone" sofa, the ingenious self-skinning polyurethane seating sold by the meter, had to be removed from production because of surface hardening and cracking. Polyurethane foam does not age well and cannot be restored, nor can it be recycled or disposed of without harm to the environment. Other foams, such as Waterlily™ (pages 74 and 75), are threatening polyurethane's monopoly in the upholstered-furniture industry. Designers have devised new stratagems to improve softness and bounce; some new techniques include gas- or air-filled polyurethane bladders like those used in sports equipment and walking shoes, and silicon-gel-filled bags, which are usually covered by cushion upholstery.

Opposite: Stephen Peart, of Vent Design. "Animal" Wet Suit (detail).

Cini Boeri. "Serpentone" Sofa. 1970 (1970). Polyurethane, sold by length. Manufactured by Arflex S.p.a., Italy.

Rubber and Foam

Because of their softness and adherence—whether used alone or as component parts of objects—rubber, foam, and gels are chosen for use in many products that come in contact with the human body. A new, seemingly fragile blue jellylike substance, with a strange appearance and peculiar touch, has become popular in the production of padding. A tough viscoelastic polymer, it cannot be pulled apart; is unaffected when pierced; and will not break, leak, dry up, or harden. Among the many ways of achieving a comfortable fit, in addition to structurally soft gel, is the use of resin bladders filled with gas or air.

Wayman R. Spence (American, b. 1934). "UltraSoft® Blue Gel Comfort Pad." 1994 (1994). Manufactured by WRS SportsMed, a division of WRS Group, Inc., United States.

Thermo-injected UltraSoft (viscoelastic-polymeric) gel, 3/4 x 16 x 16" (1.9 x 40.6 x 40.6 cm).

The manufacturer of thermo-injected UltraSoft Blue Gel suggests that it "generously cushions the body like a natural fat pad." When a heavy weight presses on an isolated area of the gel, the pressure is absorbed and redistributed over the entire surface area. Polymeric silicon compositions (whose complex chemistry is kept secret by the manufacturers) have wide-ranging applications, from hospital bed padding to the seats of automobiles and bicycles (left).

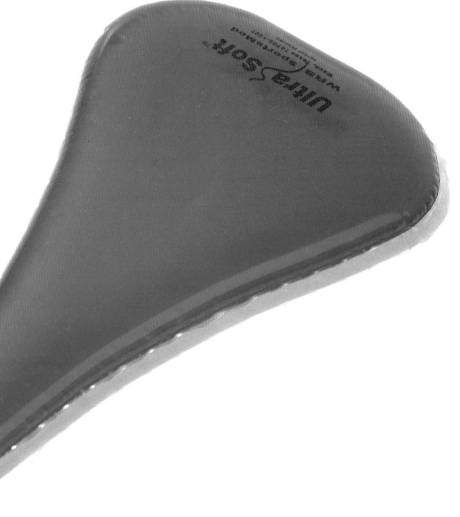

Marty Holloway (American, b. 1964) and Gary Erickson (American, b. 1957). "O₂ Air™ 40" and "O₂ AirGel™ 50" Bicycle Saddles. 1992 (1991). Manufactured by Avocet, Inc., United States.

Closed-cell polyurethane foam, gel, titanium, impact-modified nylon shell, and Lycra cover; 2 1/2 x 6 x 11" (6.4 x 15.2 x 27.9 cm) each.

Marty Holloway and Gary Erickson's technologically advanced bicycle saddles (left) illustrate the extreme properties of synthetic foams and gels. The saddles feature Avocet's ThicThin® anatomic shell, whose thick areas preserve structural integrity while its thin ones, under contact with the rider's hip bone and coccyx, control flex for maximum support and shock absorption. Integrity and flex are maintained through the use of gel cushioning. The supporting structure, the titanium ShortRail™ system, is built of Ti6AI-4V titanium manufactured to aerospace standards.

Andrew Jones (American, b. 1959), Carl Madore (American, b. 1966), David Chastain (American, b. 1952), and Harvey Koselka (American, b. 1964) of Design Continuum. "Airflex™" Baseball Glove. 1991 (1991). Manufactured by Spalding Sports Worldwide, United States.

Lycra-covered neoprene, RF (radio-frequency) welded polyurethane air system, and full-grain leather shell and liner; dimensions vary.

The air-inflation device of the "Airflex" baseball glove allows every player to achieve a custom fit. With a technology similar to that used in many athletic shoes, a player pumps the "S" button on the side of the glove to inflate the bladder. To loosen the glove, a player merely pushes the button next to the "S" for deflation. The "Airflex" is made of full-grain leather and neoprene-foam rubber. A Lycra jersey skin for suppleness is added to the flex points of the palm and the stretch areas of the glove back.

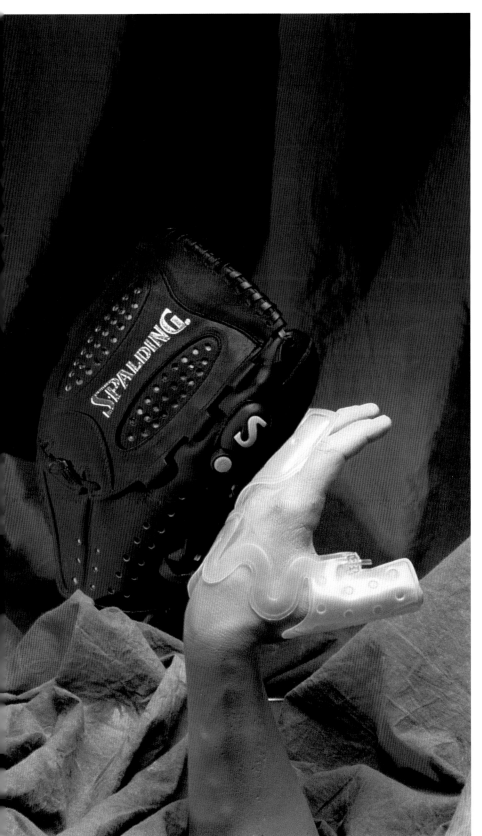

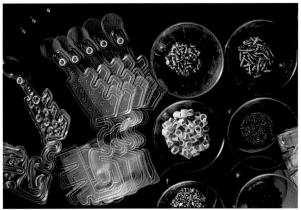

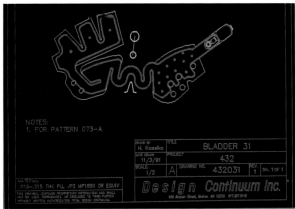

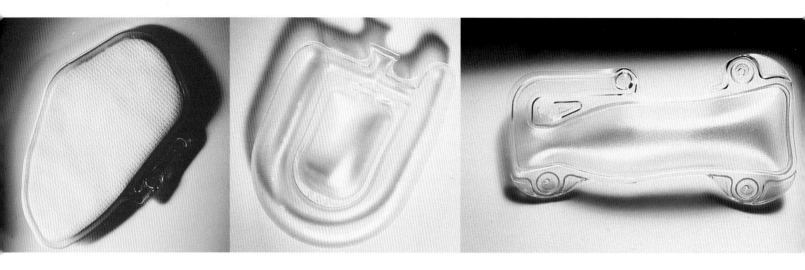

Nike Product Design. "Air Go LWP™" (Lightweight Performance) Athletic Shoe. 1994 (1993). Manufactured by Nike, Inc., United States.

Solid-rubber outsole, Phylon® (ethylvinylacetate) foam midsole, "Visible Air™" heel, "Tensile-Air™" (urethane film and three-dimensional mesh fabric) forefoot, and synthetic rubber; dimensions vary.

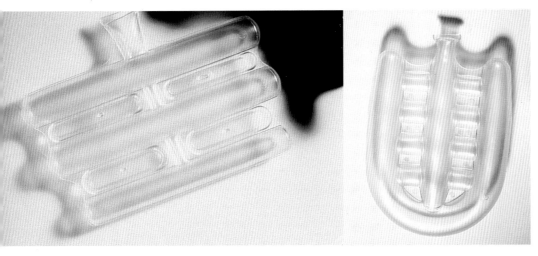

Nike Product Design. "Nike-Air®" Blow-molded Urethane Cushionings. 1994 (1993). Manufactured by Nike, Inc., United States.

"Air Max²™," "Tensile-Air™," "Nike-Air®," low-pressure "Nike-Air®," and "Flexile-Air™"; various dimensions.

Nike-Air technology uses in-sole urethane bladders in sports shoes to provide comfort and protection from forceful impact. The gas-filled bladders create a much lighter cushion than that traditionally used in midsoles. The compressed gas encapsulated in the tough urethane membrane reduces the shock of impact. After each step, the bladder returns to its original shape. In developing Nike-Air, engineers studied the various performance results of different kinds of cushioning materials. The research findings produced Air Max² (opposite center), a dual-pressure cushion that combines four individual chambers—rather than one—with two different air pressures. The lateral chambers on the perimeter of the sole are inflated to stabilize the firm-heel weight load; this pressure is greater than the medial chambers in the interior of the sole that soften cushioning and landing. Nike's Flexile-Air (above left)— used in running, basketball, and court-sport footwear—includes deep flex grooves that promote anatomically correct pliancy during every motion. Located on the forefoot of the shoe, Flexile-Air is particularly suitable for aerobic activities. Tensile-Air (opposite left) is a very thin bladder placed under the heel or forefoot or on the lateral perimeter. The cushion that uses Nike-Air blow-molded technology (above right) is produced by an injection process used to construct the AirSole unit, larger in volume and more visible than earlier sole construction. Low-pressure Nike-Air (opposite right), in a tubular shape and suitable for walking, is usually placed under the heel. An example of Nike's technology that has been integrated into a high-performance athletic shoe, the "Air Go LWP" (Lightweight Performance), specially designed for basketball play, features low-pressure Nike-Air under the heel and incorporates the Tensile-Air bladder sole in the forefoot.

Ron Arad (British, b. Israel 1951). "Misfits" Sofa. (1993).
Prototype by Moroso S.p.a., Italy.

ICI Waterlily™ foam, each
module 35 7/16 x 35 7/16 x 35 7/16"
(90 x 90 x 90 cm).

Experimentation with upholstery
foams has been in a state of limbo
since the 1960s, when the cold-
pouring technique for molding
polyurethane foam was developed.
Advances have been made only in
refining major mechanical
imperfections in the grain and
in the problem of aging and
disintegration. The recent invention
of water-based ICI Waterlily has
been achieved by developing new
raw-base materials that avoid the
use of chlorofluorocarbons (CFCs)
and other substances harmful to
the environment. Waterlily is not
molded but rather raised like
dough, cut, and carved. Two base
components are mixed with water;
expansion occurs through the same
basic principle as yeast in bread
making. The components of
Waterlily are mixed with a small
amount of catalyst and immediately
poured onto a moving paper
conveyor. The reaction creates
carbon-dioxide gas, which causes
the liquid to rise, while heat from
the chemical reaction transforms
the water into a vapor, further
increasing expansion. A uniform,
continuous block is formed,
typically about 40 x 80 in.
(100 x 200 cm), which may then
be sliced into any size or shape.
Waterlily has a microscopic
honeycomb structure composed of
small spherical bubbles, formed
during component mixing; the
bubbles increase in size during the
chemical reaction and form an
intricate network of open cells.
The material can easily be
recycled, either by rebonding or
transformation through extrusion
into an elastomeric substance. To
launch Waterlily, ICI invited a group
of furniture manufacturers and
designers to produce prototypes.
The results were mounted in an
exhibition in Milan in 1993,
organized by Silvana Sermisoni and
Studio GA Architetti Associati, where
the sofa (opposite) by Ron Arad was
displayed along with eleven
prototypes by other designers.

Christopher Connell (Australian, b. 1954) of MAP International.
"Pepe" Chair. 1993 (1992). Manufactured by MAP (Merchants
of Australian Products Pty., Ltd.), Australia.

Chlorofluorocarbon-free injection-
molded polyurethane foam, self-
skinning polyurethane, wool
upholstery, steel-spring support,
and steel frame;
51 3/16 h. x 19 11/16"
(130 h. x 50 cm dia.).

The quirky "Pepe" chair, designed
and manufactured in Australia by
Christopher Connell and Raoul
Hogg, employs a CFC-free
polyurethane foam. The lightweight
steel frame, with a spring at the
convergence of seat and back,
is clamped into a mold and
injected with foam. The hard
polyurethane legs are attached
after the upholstery is fitted.

Renzo Piano (Italian, b. 1937) and Noriaki Okabe (Japanese, b. 1947) of Renzo Piano Building Workshop. Kansai International Airport Lobby Seating. 1994 (1993). Manufactured by Okamura Corporation, Japan.

Molded polyurethane foam, steel, aluminum, artificial leather with proteins, and beech-veneer plywood; 29 7/8 x 137 x 58" (75.8 x 348 x 147.2 cm) six-seat component.

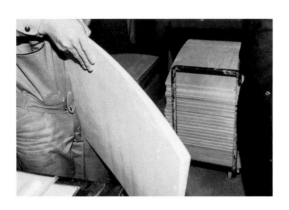

The Kansai International Airport in Osaka, Japan, is a high-tech structure celebrating green trees and blue sky. Lobby chairs and benches for the building were developed by the Osaka office of the Renzo Piano Building Workshop exclusively for the new airport. A total of 8,848 individual seats were installed in various combinations. Even though the use of polyurethane in the seating is conventional, the designers' mastery of a material in use for some time resulted in innovative shapes and solutions. In the twelve-seat unit, for example, two steel tubes on four cast-aluminum legs support two rows of six chairs placed back-to-back. The support tubing recedes visually because its coloration matches the flooring, creating the illusion of seats floating in midair. The beech-veneer plywood backs are thinned out at the upper section, reinforcing the building's theme of lightness. The polyurethane for the seat and back cushions is shaped to fit the human body. The artificial-leather upholstery material with protein additives is unusually pleasing to the touch.

Ross Lovegrove (British, b. 1958), Stephen Peart (British, b. 1958), and Knoll In-house Design Team. "Surf™ Collection" Lumbar Support. 1994 (1994). Manufactured by The Knoll Group, United States.

GECET™ (high-memory thermoreactive polyurethane foam), neoprene, nylon, and die-cast zinc counterweight; 30 3/4 x 12 1/2 x 2 3/8" (78.1 x 31.8 x 6 cm).

Back problems are alleged to be the second leading cause of lost worktime, after the common cold. Even so, in most seating construction, back supports are built of rigid, unyielding materials that ignore the diversity of the human body and its movement. Attempting to correct the absence, Ross Lovegrove and Stephen Peart have for the past ten years been involved with a new type of support foam originally developed for the aerospace industry. Used in office seating (right), the foam, which conforms to both chair back and sitter, is kept in place by a die-cast counterweight, like a saddle bag. As an office worker's weight shifts during the day, the foam responds by continually reforming itself around the sitter's body. When the chair is no longer occupied, the lumbar support returns to its original form within ten seconds, ready for the same or another occupant. The material known as GECET is a dense, high-memory, heat-reactive polyurethane foam developed for use in fighter-pilot seats. For its civilian use, GECET is covered with neoprene and a nylon outer skin.

Dynamic Systems, Inc. "Sun-Mate" and "Pudgee" Foam Cushionings. 1978 (1978). Manufactured by Dynamic Systems, Inc., United States.

Open-cell high-performance polymeric foam containing 50% vegetated materials, dimensions vary.

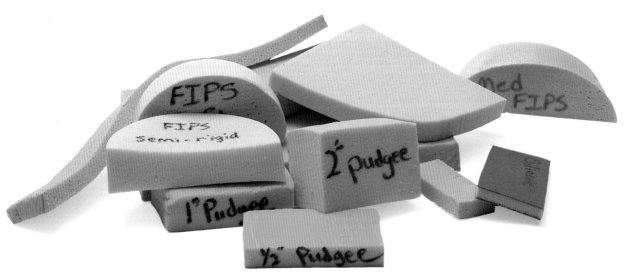

Cushioning materials from Dynamic Systems (left) belong to the same high-performance group of foams as GECET. "Sun-Mate," originally developed for the U.S. National Aeronautics and Space Administration, is a 100% high-density open-cell elastomeric foam with a density of 5 lbs./cu. ft. (80 kg/cu. m) and high-impact absorption properties. Its "slow-flow" nature embraces the body's contours and uniformly distributes a sitter's weight and pressure.

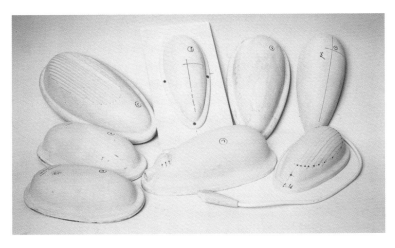

Marc Sadler (French, b. 1946). "Drop 1" and "Drop 2" Lighting Fixtures. 1994 (1993). Manufactured by Arteluce, a division of Flos S.p.a., Italy.

Injection-molded silicon-elastomer diffuser and injection-molded Lexan® polycarbonate wall support, 9 $^{11}/_{16}$ x 3 $^{3}/_{8}$ x 5" and 10 $^{1}/_{8}$ x 3 $^{15}/_{16}$ x 7 $^{1}/_{4}$" (24.6 x 8.5 x 12.7 cm and 25.6 x 9.9 x 18.4 cm), respectively.

The diffuser of Marc Sadler's lighting fixtures emits a bright glow; subtle colored illumination is projected onto the wall by the support. The soft silicon-elastomer diffuser can be removed for replacement of the energy-efficient bulb by slipping back the integrally molded rim, which acts like a taut rubber band, holding the diffuser in place on the polycarbonate support. The ribbed surface treatment on the elongated diffuser of "Drop 1" (below left) and the protuberances on the ovoid diffuser of "Drop 2" (below right) were produced in the mold.

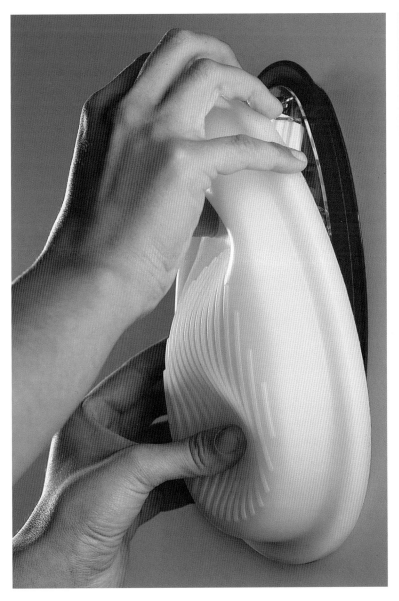

Aubert Y. Coran (American, b. 1932), Raman P. Patel (American, b. 1936), and Sabet Abdou-Sabet (American, b. 1937). Santoprene® Thermoplastic Rubber. 1981 (1981). Manufactured by Advanced Elastomer Systems, L.P., United States.

Elastomeric alloy/thermoplastic vulcanizate made from cross-linked polypropylene and EPDM (ethylene-polypropylene-diene monomer) rubber, dimensions vary.

Santoprene is a relatively new thermoplastic rubber that has become a favorite of industrial designers. Its success is due to its soft rubberlike nature and ability to be integrally colored and molded as a plastic. Santoprene begins as granular raw material (left) that can be injection-molded. Other variations, such as blow molding, extrusion, and double-shot molding, are equally possible techniques for forming Santoprene into soft or firm objects. Even though the elastomeric material is frequently formed into a solid object, it can also be applied as a thin layer over the body of another material.

Santoprene's application is appropriate where an inviting touch is desirable, such as on certain areas of frequently handled equipment, devices, and tools. For these products, Santoprene is molded into a patterned surface that both improves the grip and feels good. Santoprene was applied to areas of the "i/O," a personal digital assistant (PDA) that integrates pen- and touch-type operations with voice- and wireless-data communications (right). The hand-grip areas are also of Santoprene in frogdesign's binoculars (below).

frogdesign. Binoculars. 1990 (1988). Manufactured by Carl Zeiss Ferngläser, Germany.

Injection-molded polymers, elastomers, and other materials; 4 x 3 11/16 x 1 3/8" (10.2 x 9.3 x 3.8 cm).

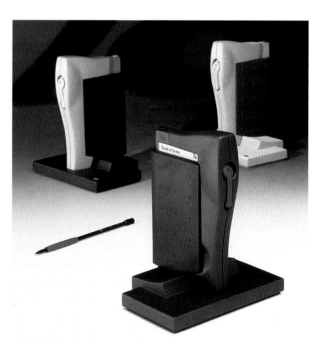

Michael Barry (American, b. 1956), Shawn Hanna (Canadian, b. 1969), and Jay Wilson (American, b. 1941) of GVO. "i/O" Personal Digital Assistant. (1994). Model.

Insert-molded Santoprene over injection-molded ABS, 13/16 x 3 1/2 x 6" (2.1 x 8.9 x 15.2 cm).

Davin Stowell (American, b. 1953), Tucker Viemeister (American, b. 1948),
Daniel Formosa (American, b. 1953), Steven Russak (American, b. 1962),
Stephan Allendorf (American, b. 1954), and Michael Callahan (American, b. 1965)
of Smart Design. "Good Grips" Utensil. 1989 (1989).
Manufactured by OXO International, United States.

Injection-molded Santoprene and
other materials, dimensions vary.
The Museum of Modern Art,
New York, gift of the designers.

The handle of the "Good Grips"
range of household and gardening
tools is composed of molded
Santoprene (above). Elastomers
were selected for their softness,
warmth, and durability. The
precision with which Santoprene
can be molded is revealed by the
ingenious striations named
Fingerprints™. These grips bend to
cushion at the point where fingers
firmly press. This makes it easier to
grasp by the elderly or infirm.

Peter Stathis (American, b. 1960) of Virtual Studio.
"Thumb Sparing" Ski-Pole Grip. (1991). Prototype.

Double-shot injection-molded
Santoprene, 6 15/16 x 4 1/4 x 2 1/2"
(17.6 x 10.7 x 6.3 cm).

For the hand grip on Peter Stathis's
ski-pole prototype (right),
Santoprene was injection-molded in
two shots in order to form firmness
at the heel of the palm area and
softness at the thumb point. To
achieve different densities in the
formation of a one-piece object,
molten material is injected into a
steel mold; then the part is shuttled
into a second steel mold into which
more material is added, which cools
in a flexible form. The final object
is released as a protective grip that
is fit by force onto the shaft of the
pole. In the future, the grips may be
molded to fit different hand sizes.

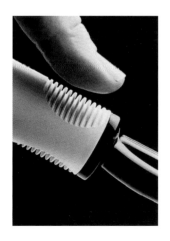

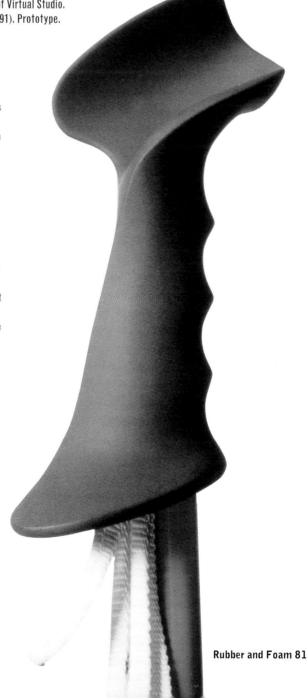

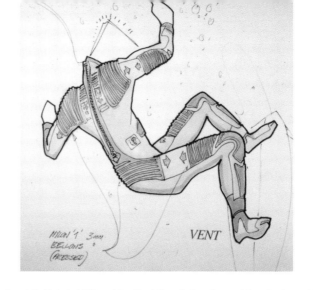

Stephen Peart (British, b. 1958) and Bradford Bissell (American) of Vent Design. "Animal" Wet Suit. 1989 (1988). Manufactured by O'Neill, Inc., United States.

Molded neoprene rubber, thermoplastic elastomer, nylon jersey, and Delrin® zipper; dimensions vary.

Rubatex, a large American manufacturer of neoprene, cast the foamed neoprene for the "Animal" wet suit for O'Neill, Inc., under a system developed by Vent Design, using a high-pressure nitrogen-injection process. The suit's design owes its success to the studies of the kinetics of the human body and the advanced technological development of synthetic-rubber injection and molding processes. From the beginning of neoprene's use in wet-suit production, designers have faced almost impossible construction problems. In order to maintain body heat, the neoprene must be as thick as possible. On the other hand, in order to accommodate body movement, it must be as thin as possible. The O'Neill Expansion System®, a molding system for producing bellowslike sections for use in high-flex areas, was developed to form accordion pleats that permit unencumbered movement. Before this, closed-cell neoprene had never been molded. Assembly of the suit requires 120 person-hours, since each one must be handcut with scissors.

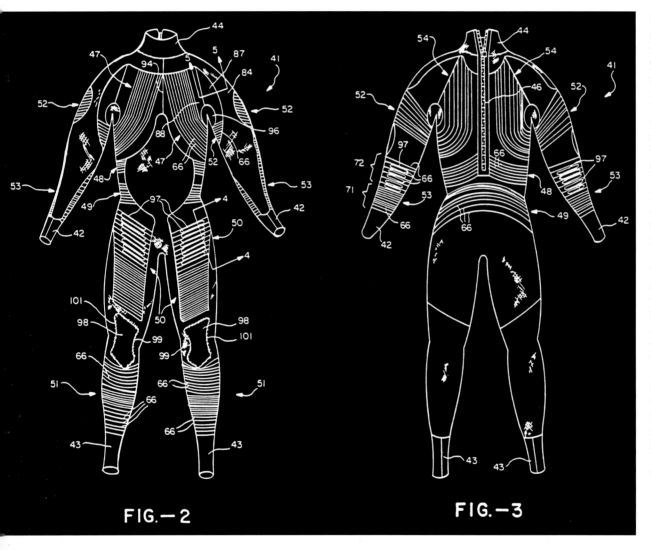

FIG.—2   FIG.—3

Marc Sadler (French, b. 1946). Motorcyclist's "Bap" Back Protector. 1993 (1992). Manufactured by Dainese S.p.a., Italy.

Expanded-polyethylene base, low-memory-foam inner padding, expanded-polyurethane pads, and polypropylene cup protector; 24 1/32 x 16 9/16" (61 x 42 cm).

Marc Sadler designed a series of protective pads for Dainese, a company renowned among motorcyclists for its earlier designs for body protection. The pads are similar to the "Animal" wet suit in appearance and function. The "Bap" back protector is a combination of several parts: the base component in expanded polyethylene anatomically shaped to conform to a rider's body, an inner section of low-memory expanded polyurethane for shock absorbency, and an outer shell in highly flexible polypropylene to protect the soft innards beneath. Smaller pad sections are placed at knee and elbow areas.

Masayuki Kurokawa (Japanese, b. 1937). "Gom" Pen. 1992 (1992).
Manufactured by Fuso Gum Industry Co., Ltd., Japan.

Synthetic rubber, stainless steel,
and brass; 7 l. x $^2/_3$" dia.
(17.6 l. x 1.5 cm dia.).

In the 1970s, Masayuki Kurokawa
began designing the "Gom" series
of tabletop objects using a
traditional type of vulcanized
rubber. Sold worldwide, these
pieces, among them a pen (left)
and a series of pushpins (below),
are some of his most recent.

Masayuki Kurokawa (Japanese, b. 1937). "Gom" Push Pins. 1985 (1984).
Manufactured by Fuso Gum Industry Co., Ltd., Japan.

Synthetic rubber and stainless steel,
1 h. x $^9/_{16}$" dia. (2.5 h. x 1.5 cm dia.).

Glass, like ceramics, has throughout history been capable of mysterious and evanescent expressions of beauty in objects. Yet glass cannot escape the plans that engineers have in store for most materials (except possibly wood and marble) as intelligent information carriers. "The future of glass may lie in information storage, where information, images, and patterns might be stored invisibly in sheets of glass only to be revealed by another process," suggests James Carpenter, an architect by training and an expert on supercooled noncrystalline solids. His glass structures have "focused on the interstitial area between exterior and interior to create a new spatial dimension with glass and light in architectural application." Carpenter exploits all the techniques for light modulation, especially dichroic coating, a film that, when applied to sheet glass, filters only two colors of the spectrum.

Glass can store information in a range of ways, from photographic impressions retrieved by hydrofluoric acid to the optical fibers discovered in 1955 by Narinder S. Kapany. And it can be combined with ceramics to form heat-resistant materials that look like glass but contain crystals smaller than the wave length of the light that passes through them, and thus are invisible. This very strong glass is used, for example, in the production of stove tops, ironically recalling the birth of glass from fire.

In addition to coatings on glass sheets and additives to the fusion process, other glass products are created by the insertion of a second material between two sheets of glass. For example, glass panels for controlling and redirecting natural light are separated by filtering aluminum louvers or honeycombs, or by plastic rods (pages 90 and 91). Also, sandwich panels become opaque when the liquid crystals within are activated by electricity. And still other glass, used in fire doors, contains a gel that becomes irreversibly opaque and fire-resistant when exposed to excessive heat.

The variety and applications of glass are infinite. Current experiments are wide-ranging and even extend to the idea of cooling glass in space for better results. While science fiction becomes routine, other designers are turning to the most traditional glass technologies and shapes, such as the blow-molded glass-bowl hanging lamp (page 92), to translate them into a contemporary idiom.

Opposite: Soda Bottle. c. 1941. Glass, 10 x 3" (22 x 6.5 cm). Manufacturer unknown (Italy).

James Carpenter, Janet Fink, Richard Kress, Neil Logan, and Luke Lowings. *Tension Net Sculpture*. 1990. Dichroic glass, 100' (33 m) long. Project for Southern California Gas Co., Los Angeles.

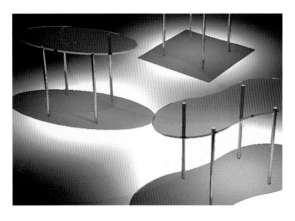 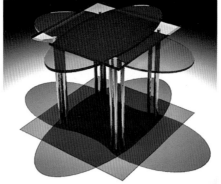 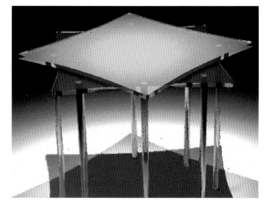

Karim England Rashid (Canadian, b. Egypt 1960). "Aura" Coffee Table. (1990). Prototype.

$^1/_2$" (1.5 cm) glass, colored PMMA (polymethyl-methacrylate) film, steel rods, and redwood; $17\,^3/_4$ x $18\,^{15}/_{16}$ x $33\,^1/_2$" (45 x 48 x 85 cm).

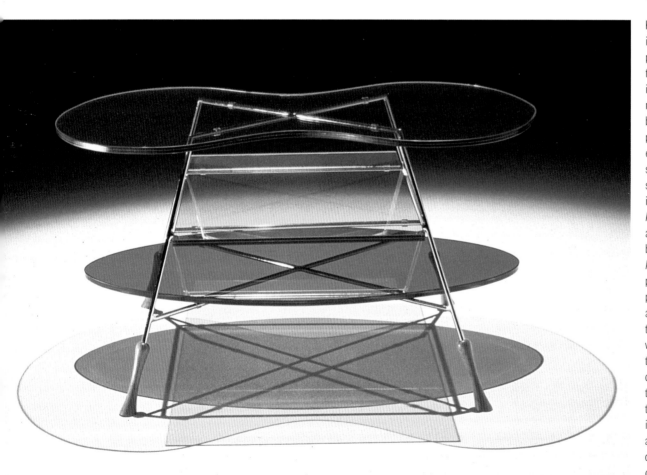

Karim Rashid's "Aura" coffee table is a spontaneous exploration of the potentialities of laminated glass technology. Rashid used PMMA film in his project, yet one of any number of other films could have been used to achieve other polarizing, refractive, and optical effects. In a "clean room," two stacked glass sheets were cut in a shape according to preset instructions from a computer. A super-thin pellicle of PMMA, available in 1,600 tints, was placed between the two layers of glass. A super-high-pressure laminating press fused the three layers into a pertectic state (between a solid and a liquid) and metamorphosed the sandwich into a solid sheet, whose edges were polished to hide the film layer. When viewed from different perspectives, one side of the sheet appears different from the other. The "Aura" coffee table is designed to be configured into approximately twenty-seven different compositions (see computer drawings above) made possible by different colors and shapes of glass on three levels.

Schott Laboratory Systems. "Safe-I-Duct™" Glass Ductwork. 1994 (1993).   Borosilicate glass, dimensions vary.
Manufactured by Schott Process Systems, Inc., United States.

"Safe-T-Duct" ductwork, made of borosilicate glass, provides an effective alternative to stainless-steel pipes. Like other glass made with silicates and boron, the ductwork has a high resistance to chemical corrosives and temperature changes and is appropriate for use in numerous chemical- and pharmaceutical-industry applications. As a component in the ventilation systems of chemical laboratories, where the safe exhaustion of corrosive gases is required, "Safe-T-Duct" facilitates easy accessibility to fume-hood controls.

Borosilicate glass is also used in the manufacture of ampules, medicine bottles, and high-intensity electric light bulbs. "Safe-T-Duct" is produced by the Vello process, a procedure for drawing glass tubing from a furnace forehearth; molten glass flows down through a ring while the hollow space in the diameter of the tube is kept constant by a pipe with a conical opening located within the ring. The glass tubing, while still soft, is redirected horizontally and drawn off along a roller track, cooled, and cut into 60 in. (150 cm) lengths.

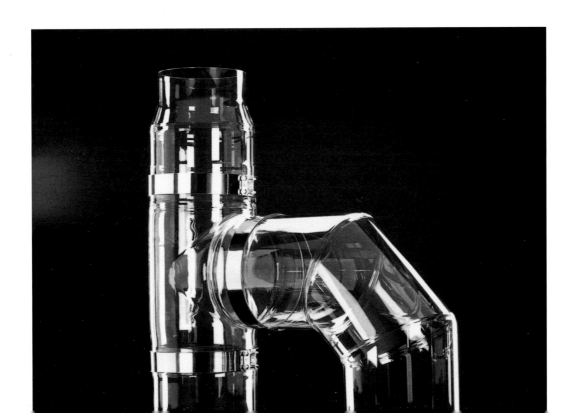

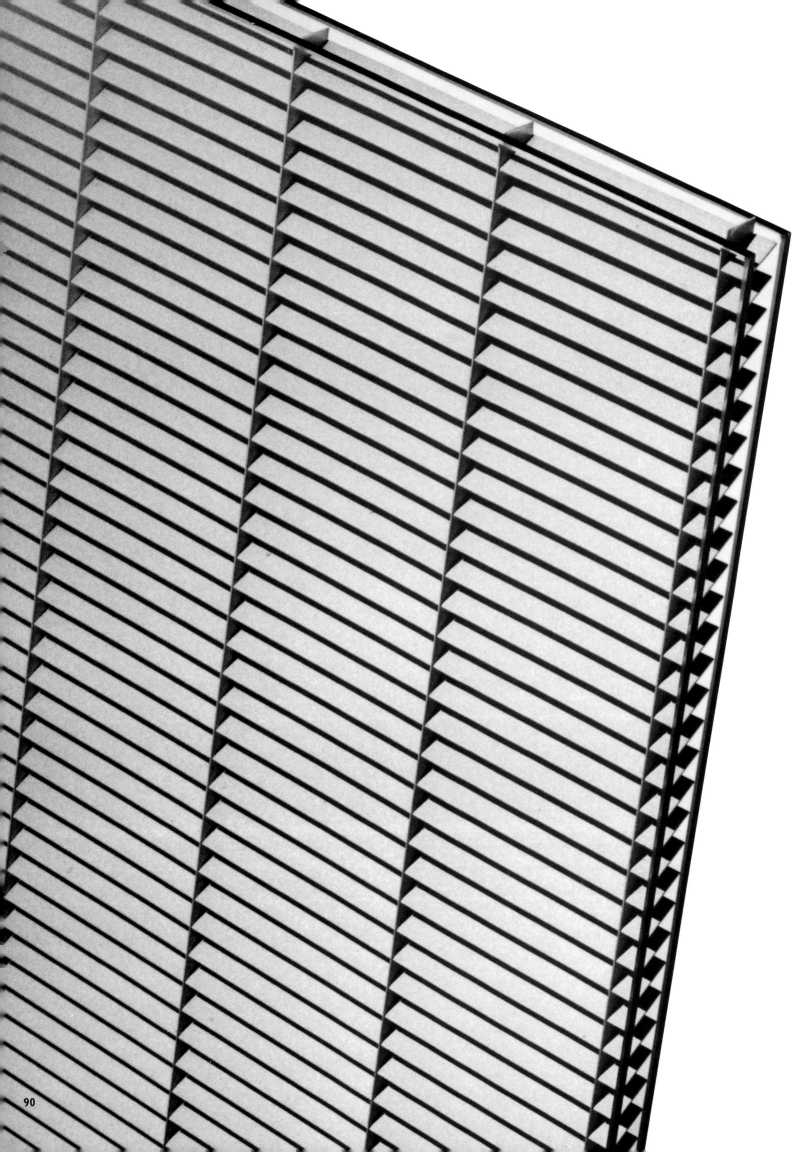

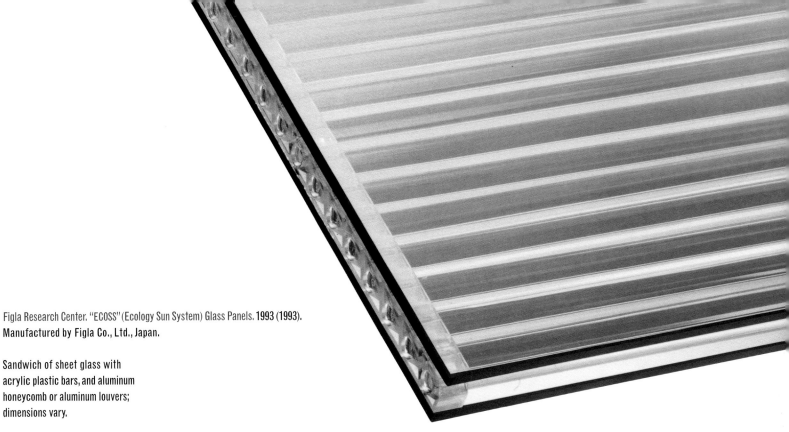

Figla Research Center. "ECOSS" (Ecology Sun System) Glass Panels. 1993 (1993).
Manufactured by Figla Co., Ltd., Japan.

Sandwich of sheet glass with
acrylic plastic bars, and aluminum
honeycomb or aluminum louvers;
dimensions vary.

Development of the "ECOSS" system
was based on research in the
reduction of solar-heat gain in
interior spaces during the summer
and the absorption of solar heat
during the winter. The "ECOSS"
system is used to filter sunlight on
the curtain wall of a building but is
also appropriate for light and airy
interior-space dividers that offer
privacy. In addition, it can be used
for skylights and sloped roof
panels. A highly effective control of
sunlight, "ECOSS" uses a transparent
filter that maintains room brightness
by scattering sun rays, uniformly
fragmenting and distributing glare.
The window panel, installed like a
normal pane of glass, is a sandwich
of core bodies sealed along the
perimeter of two sheets of glass.
The core is composed of either
plastic sections that are round or
triangular axially, aluminum
honeycombs, or aluminum louvers.
Within the sandwich, the angles of
the louvers or plastic sections are
uniquely inclined and adjusted. The
adjustment is made according to
the sunlight cast on the facade of a
specific building, based on the
geographic orientation and angle
of inclination of the windows as
well as the sun's angles of
incidence; the sun is high in the sky
in summer and low in winter. The
refractive and reflective angles of
the sunlight are simulated in the
computer, and the most effective
control angle is determined.

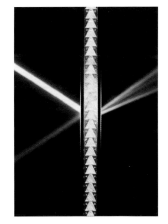

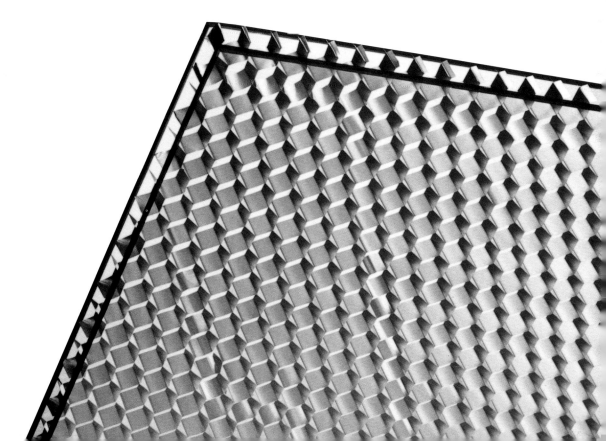

Achille Castiglioni (Italian, b. 1918). "Brera" Lighting Fixture. 1992 (1992). Manufactured by Flos S.p.a., Italy. Acid-treated blown glass, 12 5/8 h. x 7 7/8" dia. (32 h. x 20 cm dia.). The Museum of Modern Art, New York, gift of the manufacturer.

The "Brera" hanging light took its inspiration from the painting, *The Madonna and Child with Federico da Montefeltro,* c. 1475, by Piero della Francesca, in the Pinacoteca di Brera in Milan, Italy. In the painting an ostrich egg, a symbol of the virgin birth, is suspended over the Madonna's head. In Achille Castiglioni's lighting fixture, available in models for ceiling suspension, wall mounting, or floor placement, the diffuser emulates the egg. The lamp is a distinctive interpretation of the classic opaline-glass sphere. The "egg" is made of acid-treated blown glass, split into two horizontal sections held together by a ring nut for easy bulb access and ventilation, mounted on a steel cable, and electrified by two thin wires.

Bernard Alain Brux (French, b. 1950) and Philippe Gourdon (French, b. 1955). "Mano" Lighting Fixture. 1991 (1989). Manufactured by Luxo Italiana S.p.a., Italy.

Acid-etched blown glass and stamped sheet metal, 7 5/16 x 4 3/4 x 3 3/16" (18.5 x 12 x 8 cm).

Like the "Brera" (opposite), the "Mano" lamp is a minimal interpretation of the traditional opaline-glass diffuser. The cast-glass diffuser is attached to an aluminum support by three small steel brackets. The glass is mounted flush to the wall; the inset box (below) allows the curve of the cone to be the only element that is gently pushed forward. The light source is either halogen or PL tube (9 watts or 7 watts).

James Carpenter (American, b. 1949), Luke Lowings (British, b. 1961), Richard Kress (American, b. 1962), and Janet Fink (American, b. 1961) of James Carpenter Design Associates. "Dichroic Light Field." (1994). Project for New York City, United States.

Mirror-glass panels and dichroic glass blades, 46 x 100' (14 x 30 m).

James Carpenter began his career in architecture and focused on glass for its tangible three-dimensional form and for its essence, light. He has become known for manipulating light through his use of glass in an architectural context. "Dichroic Light Field" is a proposed 46 x 100 ft. (14 x 30 m) billboard artwork to be installed at the northwest corner of 68th Street and Columbus Avenue in Manhattan in New York City. Composed of two parts, the panel will be clad with diffused-mirror-glass panels that project a field of light created by narrow blades of dichroic glass protruding from the surface of the diffused mirror panels. The dichroic blades capture and project daylight and color in a pattern that changes with the time of day, varying seasonally. At night, sharp-focused lighting fixtures illuminate the panels from below.

James Carpenter (American, b. 1949), Luke Lowings (British, b. 1961), Richard Kress (American, b. 1962), Janet Fink (American, b. 1961), and Neil Logan (American, b. 1959) of James Carpenter Design Associates. "Arch Truss Wall." (1991). Project for Los Angeles Center, United States.

Planar™ glass by Pilkington and stainless-steel fittings.

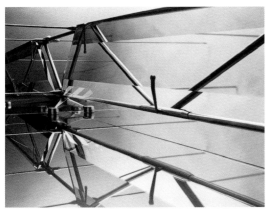

James Carpenter developed "Arch Truss Wall" for Los Angeles Center, a building designed by architects Johnson, Fain, and Pereira. The glass installation is comprised of two curved curtain walls, facing southeast and southwest, and functions as a self-supporting structure. The eight steel arches are composed of a series of stainless-steel trusses combined with integrated, machined glass blades. In depths from 20 in. (50 cm) at the exposed extreme end to 9 in. (20 cm) at the center, where an overhang shields the wall from the sun, the exterior glass uses the Planar System by Pilkington Glass, Ltd.

James Carpenter (American, b. 1949), Luke Lowings (British, b. 1961), Richard Kress (American, b. 1962), and Janet Fink (American, b. 1961) of James Carpenter Design Associates. "Refractive Tensegrity Rings." Munich Airport, Germany. 1993. Commissioned by BMW AG, Germany.

Dichroic coated-glass panels and stainless-steel fittings, 22' (7 m) dia.

BMW commissioned Carpenter's "Refractive Tensegrity Rings," an installation for the main concourse of Munich's new airport. The rings measure almost 22 ft. (7 m) in diameter. Highly subtle stainless-steel fittings and rods compress the dichroic-coated glass panels to form a rigid truss. All components are prototypes, pre-assembled in sections. The machined stainless-steel parts, almost disappearing from sight when installed, were manufactured in the United States and shipped to Germany.

Among materials, wood is the most discreet. It has not participated in the industrial era's major technological breakthroughs. Even when advances have been achieved, they have been hidden by wood's serene permanence.

As with other materials, engineering efforts aimed at pushing wood beyond its natural limitations have primarily involved its transformation into moldable compounds capable of producing homogenous, isotropic materials. Driven by economic goals, full-scale production of wood-composite panels began in the 1960s. The examples shown in this section illustrate the lively search for new composites. They range from the very coarse particleboard pallet that Ali Tayar chose for the manufacture of the table on page 101 and the compound Philippe Starck specified for his television set (pages 104 and 105) to the imaginative Maderón, which is made from almond shells and other lignocellulosic substances (pages 102 and 103).

Quite different from saw-dust composites are laminates and veneers, among which is Softwood™, developed by the aeronautical industry. It is composed of natural wood laminated onto fabric and applied directly to foam. Also exploiting laminated wood's malleability, Frank Gehry's seating for Knoll (page 100) is composed of a series of structural ribbons of bent maple.

Many objects seemingly only of plastic, metal, or wood are often composites of various materials, although they are frequently named for their principal component. For this reason, the wood-core snowboard and hockey sticks reinforced with socks and blankets of glass and graphite fibers have been included in this section (pages 106 and 107).

Finnish cabinetmaker Kari Virtanen says, "I have learned that we have very little knowledge of wood, and there is not very much research being done. We have to submit ourselves to the conditions of wood." His modest attitude testifies to the power of wood, possibly the only material still able to maintain its absolute position, related more to nature than to artifice.

Opposite: Pre-cut lumber used in furniture manufacturing.

Wood

Marco Ferreri (Italian, b. 1958). "Less" Chair and "Is" Stool. 1994 (1993). Manufactured by Nemo S.r.l., Italy. Die-pressed Softwood™, polyurethane foam, and beech; 29 1/2 x 18 1/2 x 17 3/4" (75 x 47 x 45 cm) chair; 17 3/4 x 15 3/4 x 13 3/4 (45 x 40 x 35 cm) stool.

The chair and stool designs by Marco Ferreri utilize the technology of Softwood, a material that is a laminate of fabric and wood. The fabric and wood layers are thermally bonded and molded under pressure and padded with a sheet of polyurethane foam. A soft, flexible, surprising seating surface is created. The polyurethane sheet is placed only in the central part of the seat and back, and the Softwood is attached at the perimeter by hot die-pressing. The fabric becomes soft and acts as an adhesive at high temperatures, eliminating the need for a glue additive. Ferreri's symbolically minimal design statement places technology on a pedestal. The manufacturer, Nemo, has been assigned the exclusive rights to the process for the furniture industry, although a technologically advanced material similar to Softwood has appeared in the production of leather fashion accessories.

Krohn Design. "Tuffet" Stool. 1994 (1994). Manufactured by Abbott Enterprises, United States.

Maple plywood, closed-cell polyurethane foam, stainless steel, and mohair velvet upholstery; 21 1/2 h. x 12 1/2" dia. (54.6 h. x 31.8 cm dia.).

The idiosyncratic "Tuffet" stool—looking like a beehive, wriggling with its sitter, and evoking nursery-rhyme memories of Little Miss Muffet—"is designed to touch the child in everybody," according to its designer. To achieve its playful appearance, a 3/4 in. (2 cm) 13-ply maple-veneer plywood sheet is cut into squares, and a router with a template forms twelve doughnut-shaped rings of varying diameters, three with protrusions to form a handle. The wood rings divide alternating circles of closed-cell polyurethane foam, which have been rough-cut with a band saw and trimmed by a router. The completed seat is sanded, clear finished, and glued. The top ring is fitted with a velvet-covered foam cushion, removable for access to a snug hideaway. Solid stainless-steel legs are saw-cut, bent, and attached to a flat plate. Small hydraulic-press-punched stainless-steel disks are welded to the legs, which are attached to the fourth ring from the bottom.

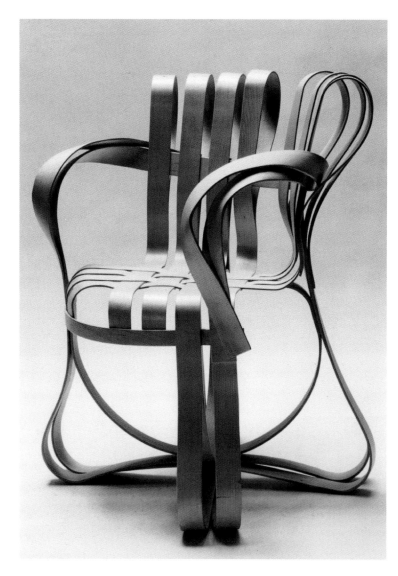

Frank O. Gehry (American, b. Canada 1929). "Cross Check" Armchair. 1992 (1990). Manufactured by The Knoll Group, United States.

High-bonding-urea laminated and bent white maple wood strips, 33 1/2 x 28 x 26 1/2" (85 x 71.1 x 67.4 cm). The Museum of Modern Art, New York, gift of the designer and the manufacturer.

With project designer Daniel Sachs and design technician Tom MacMichael, architect Frank Gehry devoted two years to the hands-on development of a new bentwood product system for The Knoll Group. The design was influenced by the traditional technology of ordinary wood crates and bushel baskets used to hold fruit and vegetables. One hundred fifteen prototypes were consolidated into five chairs, two tables, and an ottoman. With these unadorned autonomous structures, Gehry, like Alvar Aalto and Charles and Ray Eames, joins the tradition of the great modern experiments in furniture design. Gehry's work for Knoll also has stature within a contemporary aesthetic. In chair production, six to eight layers of white maple are cut into 2 in. (5.1 cm) wide and 1/32 in. (.2 cm) thick strips. The wood grain is positioned lengthwise for resilience, and the strips are laminated with high-bonding urea. The use of a recently developed thermoset assembly glue that facilitates movement and flexibility eliminates the need for nails, screws, or other metal connectors; no glue is applied to the springy, comfortable woven seats. The largest chair weighs only about 8 pounds (3.62 kg).

Frank O. Gehry (American, b. Canada 1929). "Power Play" Armchair. 1992 (1991). Manufactured by The Knoll Group, United States.

High-bonding-urea laminated and bent white maple wood strips, 32 3/4 x 30 1/2 x 31 1/2" (83.2 x 77.5 x 80 cm). The Museum of Modern Art, New York, gift of the designer and the manufacturer.

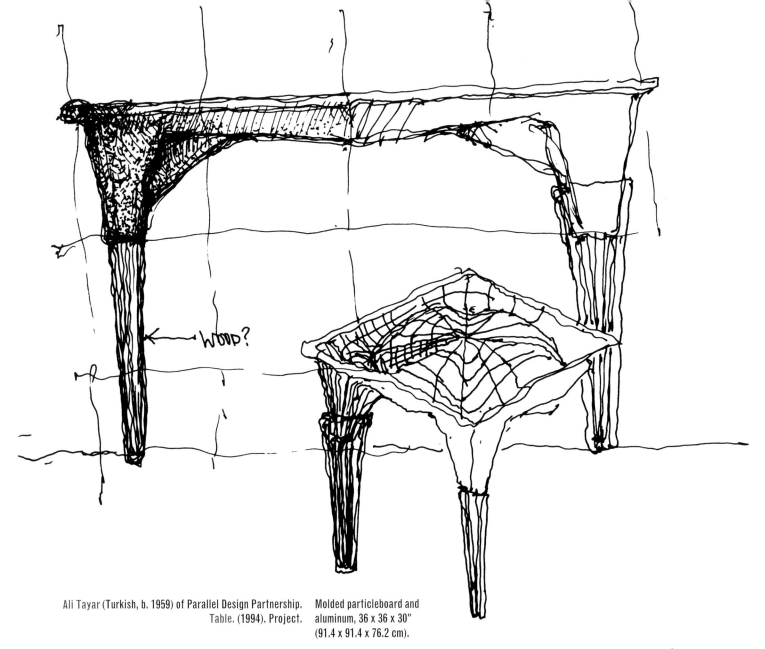

Ali Tayar (Turkish, b. 1959) of Parallel Design Partnership.
Table. (1994). Project.

Molded particleboard and
aluminum, 36 x 36 x 30"
(91.4 x 91.4 x 76.2 cm).

Recomposed, moldable wood has an essential structure that becomes plastic while the truth of the material is altered. The production process entails the transformation of fibers into particles of different calibers that are used to form various materials. The compounds range from very fine, heavy, medium-density-fiber (MDF) board, introduced in the late 1970s, to rougher grinds, like that used in Ali Tayar's table. To create the quintessential ready-made object and also develop a system of affordable furniture, he chose a stock particleboard pallet of the type used in the food industry for transporting goods to market. This coarse material, made from recycled wood shavings, is molded into a "structural expression," according to the designer, in a shape dictated by function. Fitted with die-cast aluminum legs, the dining table (above) is topped with a sheet of clear glass that exposes the industrial object beneath.

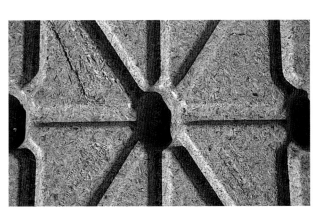

Juan Biosca (Spanish, b. 1949) and Ramón Ubeda (Spanish, b. 1962). Maderón™ composite material,
"Silia" Modular Seating. 1994 (1994). 45 x 40 x 44"
Manufactured by Lignocel S.a., Spain. (114.3 x 101.6 x 111.7 cm).

Antoni Gaudí (Spanish, 1852–1926). "Batlló" Chair (detail).
Originally designed for the Casa Batlló, Barcelona. 1994 (1906).
Manufactured by Gauhaus, Spain.

Maderón composite material,
29 1/2 x 20 1/2 x 19 3/4"
(73 x 52 x 50 cm).

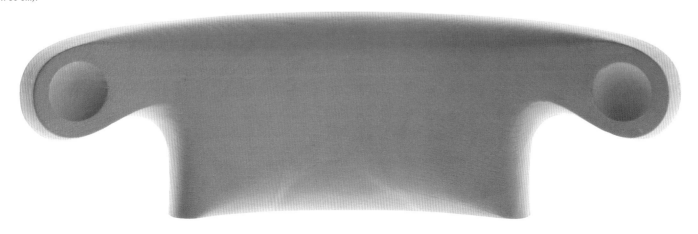

**Almond shells and other
lignocellulosic materials,
dimensions vary.**

Maderón, an example of the inventive use of lignocellulosic particles, was invented by chemical engineer Silio Cardona, who also developed its fabrication and application processes. (Maderón is Spanish for a large piece of wood.) In 1980, he discovered that the almond harvesting industry in Spain, which is second only to the United States in production, annually discards more than 300,000 short tons of the shells after the nuts are removed. Cardona realized the potential the refuse had as a raw, though unusual, material. He conceived of making cast objects from a mixture of resin and a paste of crushed almond shells and other lignocellulosic materials. The resulting material, Maderón, can be produced in a range of densities from 30 to 1,000 gm per liter; has the appearance of fine, light-colored wood; features the malleability of plastics; can be treated to become heat-resistant; is weatherproof and environmentally friendly; and, like thermoplastics, can be injection-molded. Maderón has been employed in the manufacture of a number of diverse objects, including the souvenir sombrero (right), at the

Museo Teatro Dalí in Figueras, Spain, and for some contemporary and period-revival furniture. Among contemporary furniture made of Maderón, the "Rothko" chair (left) by Alberto Liévore is molded in two parts: a section for the backrest and rear legs, and one for the seat and front legs. The "Batlló" chair, based on a 1906 design by Antoni Gaudí for the Casa Batlló in Barcelona, was reproduced in 1994 in Maderón (opposite bottom). Gaudí's original chairs are carved in solid oak; Maderón has made it possible to reduce the chair's weight and cost. Questionable poetic license may have been taken in re-issuing this design classic, which retains only the shape but not the original substantial nature and handmade character of the original. On the other hand, its reproduction does make a case for the innovative recycling of raw materials.

Alberto Liévore (Argentine, b. 1948). "Rothko" Chair. 1994 (1989).
Manufactured by Indartu, Spain.

Maderón composite material,
28 3/4 x 20 7/8 x 19 11/16"
(73 x 53 x 50 cm).

Interior view, Casa Batlló, Barcelona,
1906, showing original "Batlló" chair.

Philippe Starck (French, b. 1949). "Jim Nature" Television Set. 1993 (1993).
Manufactured by Thomson Consumer Electronics, France, for Saba, France.

Sawdust, formol-free glue, water-based paint, and other materials;
14 3/4 x 15 3/8 x 15 3/8"
(37.5 x 39 x 39 cm).

Utilizing the possibilities of recycled-wood-particle technology, Philippe Starck's television set is an imaginative example of the sensibility and economy that can be applied to design. In Starck's words, "It seems desirable for the twentieth century to be marked by 'immaterials.' Television is primary in this regard because its contents are what really count; its shape and substance are mere messengers. Therefore, we have no legitimate excuse for wasting the earth's precious resources on television exteriors." For his television cabinet, he used sawdust. The four sections of the housing, a recycled and recyclable cage molded from resin-impregnated sawdust and wood powder, are fastened together by ordinary screws. The remote-control device is stored in a pocket molded into the thermoplastic back of the housing. A simple nylon handle, like the standard model for suitcases, facilitates the set's portability. The shipping carton is reduced to only two polystyrene-free corrugated-cardboard sides.

Some of the most interesting hybrid materials are to be found in the world of sports, where performance is essential. For example, low-tech wood can be greatly strengthened by high-tech fibers in the production of sporting equipment to resist the strain and the intense flex created by tough treatment during sporting activities.

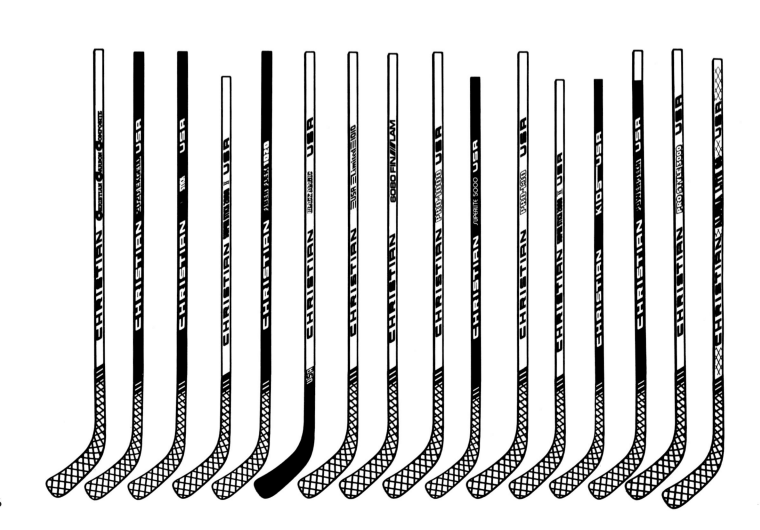

Shaw Kaake (American, b. 1962) of DNR Sportsystem. "H-Type 156 XXX" Santa Cruz Snowboard. 1994 (1993). Manufactured by Authier Ski, Switzerland.

Poplar, fiberglass, stainless-steel threaded insert, ABS, UHMW (ultra-high molecular weight) high-density polyethylene, hardened-carbon-steel edges, rubber, ABS-polyurethane blended transparent top surface with lacquer backprinted silk screening, and heat-cured epoxy resin; 61 1/2 x 10 1/2" (156 x 26.5 cm).

The snowboard industry has been the spawning ground for some of the most recent technological advances, many originating from amateur experimentation. Even though numerous major companies have attempted snowboard manufacture, those most passionate about the sport remain committed to boards made by smaller, informally organized companies. Shaw Kaake's snowboard (left) has a poplar core formed by finger joints that hold reassembled rectangular sections. Computer-numerical-control machinery is used to shape it and perforate small holes, which later receive epoxy resin. The fiberglass layers, having been saturated with epoxy resin, are placed into an aluminum cassette with preassembled sections of printed and die-cut materials. Parts of the snowboard are assembled by hand and fused in a heated hydraulic press.

The Christian Brothers. Hockey Sticks. 1984–94 (1984–94). Manufactured by The Christian Brothers, Inc., United States.

Ash core and graphite and fiberglass binding, dimensions vary.

A prime example of an essentially thin piece of wood that receives unyielding stress, the hockey sticks (opposite) by Christian Brothers have a blade whose core is made of ash. The wood is covered with the Diamond Design Slapsock®, a blend of graphite fibers braided with fiberglass. Covering the entire blade and, in some models, also the heel, the fibers increase overall strength and durability. For the "3030" model hockey stick, a solid aspen core surrounded by lightweight graphite is covered over in white ash. In other Christian Brothers sticks, the wood is replaced by a carbon composite with a seamless, continuous carbon-fiber hybrid-filament binding around the shaft, impregnated by a computer-controlled resin-transfer molding process.

Steel and aluminum are the most commonly used metals in industrial design today, and titanium and magnesium are gaining acceptance. Each metal is structurally unique, has its own melting point, and requires and allows different manufacturing methods. Each needs appropriate tooling and produces individual formal results. "Nevertheless, traditional metals are not that difficult to design and customize. You can hot-roll metals, like you do steel sections. Except for steel, you can extrude them," says Guy Nordenson, a partner in the engineering firm Ove Arup & Partners. Hot-rolling, extrusion, and die and sand casting are still the most widely available and frequently employed techniques for forming metals. Compared to plastics and glass, metal technology may appear to be limited, but there have been many recent advancements.

Nordenson says, "Very interesting developments have occurred in the design of materials in a number of fields, but the technology hasn't yet percolated down to architecture and building engineering." Even though superplastic steel forming is not yet available for the production of everyday objects, shape-memory alloys are now used in numerous domestic applications, such as eyeglasses, brassieres, and household appliances. The availability of metallic composites has been facilitated, as Nordenson suggests, by machine tools becoming "cheaper and better controlled. You can do many things today at less cost than in the past. . . . Composites are being produced with boron fiber or some other additives within a metal matrix." The enhanced tooling, which can produce expressive forms, is illustrated by the detailing in some of the objects in this section.

The demand for elasticity and lightness, initially fulfilled by harmonic steel in thin tubing and bands, has found a new resource in titanium. Its light weight and easy machinability have made it appropriate for the structural framework of vehicles, such as Michael Burrows's tricycle (page 121) and Kazuo Kawasaki's wheelchair (page 120), and for linear sections, such as those in the eyeglasses on page 113. Magnesium is another material with new-found applications; its insulating properties and easy machinability make it ideal for extruded profiles, such as those by Dow (page 115), and in computer shielding plates.

The status of metals has been eroded during the past few decades by other materials. They have been replaced by ceramics for engine parts and cutting blades, by composites in a variety of applications, including airplanes and boats, and by plastics in small-scale structures like seating. As Nordenson observes, "Materials development and usage are historically cyclical. Work with metals is probably more out of touch than it is behind."

Opposite: Extruded aluminum. Manufactured by Kaiser Aluminum Co., United States.

Smith-Miller + Hawkinson Architects and Ove Arup & Partners. Ticket Counter Canopy, USAir Terminal, La Guardia Airport, New York. 1992 (1991). Composite sandwich panel made of Nomex® core with skins of epoxy-impregnated fiberglass and carbon; 36 panels, each 7' x 14' x $^3/_4$" (213 x 426 x 19 cm).

Metals

Research and Development Department of Callaway Golf. "Big Bertha®" No. 5 Golf Iron. 1994 (1991). Manufactured by Callaway Golf Co., United States.

Stainless-steel head and Memphis 10® lightweight-steel or RCH 90™ graphite shaft, 2 x 4 1/2 x 3/4" (5.1 x 11.4 x 1.9 cm).

Golf equipment includes three categories of clubs: woods and irons, numbered according to purpose, and the putter. The head of the "Big Bertha" no. 5 iron (left) is made of stainless steel. In April 1995, a new driver in titanium was made available. The tooling employed by Callaway Golf to construct the "Big Bertha" begins with the lost-wax investment-cast process, in which the interior of a mold is filled with wax that melts when molten metal is poured into it. The tooling creates a precise cast with a constant thickness along the perimeter of the head. The finished head is connected to a hollow shaft made of Callaway's Memphis 10 steel or its RCH 90 graphite. The shaft is inserted into a socket at the end of the head and bonded with epoxy glue. The shaft extends through the head and is cut flush with the bottom sole. The grip is made of a natural rubber-based compound reinforced with a cotton-cord material. Laser-beam technology facilitates the proper alignment of the grip with the head and the shaft.

Richard Miles (British, b. 1949) and John Tree (British, b. 1969) of FM Design. Padlocks. 1993 (1992). Manufactured by Yale Security Products, Ltd., Great Britain.

CNC (computer-numerical-control) milled EN32C steel for padlock bodies, and hardened steel for shackles and rollers; dimensions vary. The Museum of Modern Art, New York, gift of the manufacturer.

For the Yale padlocks, the designers wed the basic features of an effective locking device— durability, strength, and resistance —with unusually elegant form and texture inspired by pebbles on a beach—organically shaped, water-and-sand etched, and tactilely pleasing. But more pragmatically, the locks are designed to be impossible to pick. Made from massive case-hardened steel that is milled by CNC tooling, they cannot be sawed or drilled.

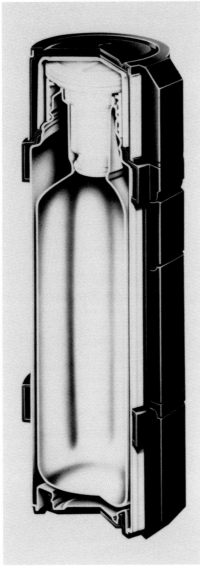

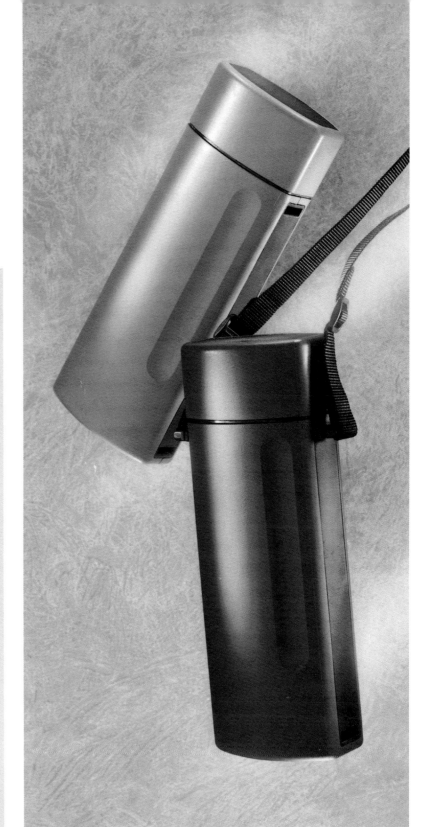

Kaori Mano (Japanese, b. 1952) of Kyoto Design Center.
"HSO 500" Thermos® Oval Vacuum Bottle. 1986 (1985).
Manufactured by Nippon Sanso Corporation, Japan.

High-vacuum-formed stainless
steel and polypropylene,
10 x 4 x 2 $^5/_8$" (25.4 x 10 x 6.5 cm).

The popular but fragile glass vacuum bottle carried in lunch boxes is a thing of the past. The inner and outer shells of vacuum bottles can now be made of unbreakable stainless steel. The oval travel version (above) includes an outer body of durable plastic. The assembly and joining methods used in these Thermos vacuum bottles eliminate the use of valves and fittings that have the potentiality of leakage. The vacuum space between the layers of steel insures long-lasting insulation properties.

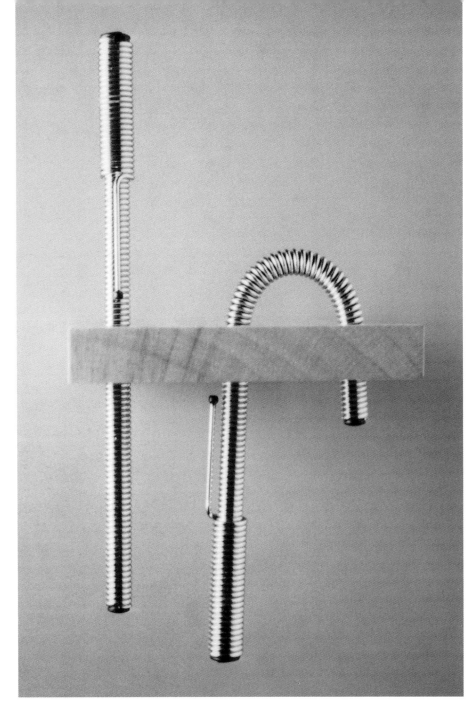

Sebastian Bergne (British, b. 1966) of Bergne: design for manufacture.
"Spira" Ballpoint Pen. 1993 (1989).
Manufactured by Ventura design on time S. A., Switzerland.

Stainless-steel winder/press
(automatic spring) and injection-
molded nylon, 5 $^1/_8$ l. x $^3/_8$" dia.
(13 l. x .9 cm dia.).

The simple components of the "Spira"
ballpoint pen (left) include a standard
spring body that allows the pen to
be bent without damage when in the
pocket of a garment or during
activity harmful to ordinary thin pens.

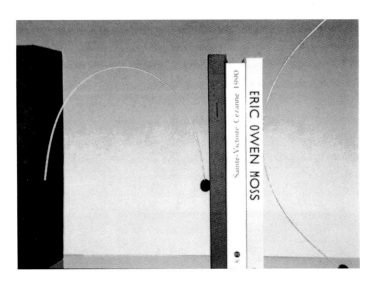

Giorgio Gurioli (Italian, b. 1957) and Francesco Scansetti
(Italian, b. 1955). "Tra" Bookends. 1992 (1991).
Manufactured by Sỳn S.r.l., Italy.

Nickel-plated steel and injection-
molded elastomer, 17 $^3/4$ x 1 x $^9/_{16}$"
(45 x 2.5 x 1.5 cm).

The "Tra" bookends (left) make use
of harmonic (high-carbon) nickel-
plated steel. Italian for "between" or
"among," the "Tra" is a springy
metallic parenthesis that holds
books upright in place and is
enclosed by two rubber cylinders.
The tension arch acts to separate
the books from the sides of a
bookcase and from each other.

Dissing + Weitling Architects and Poul-Jørn Lindberg (Danish). "AIR Titanium"
Eyeglasses. 1988 (1985). Manufactured by Lindberg Optic Design, Denmark.

**Titanium and medical silicone,
dimensions vary.**

For eyeglasses, titanium filaments achieve a sense of nothingness—the annihilation of design through its sublimation. Created by Danish architects Dissing + Weitling in collaboration with optometrist Poul-Jørn Lindberg, the "AIR Titanium" system is a unique, patented method for producing handcrafted eyeglasses in an almost infinite number of different lens shapes and colors, together with an array of temples, bridges, and connecting clips. "AIR Titanium," weighing slightly less than a single ounce (2.8 gm), has no screws, rivets, or soldering. The frames are individually adaptable to each wearer, and a person's own optician mounts the clips on the temples in a slot milled into the rimless lenses. Titanium wire in three degrees of hardness and a thickness of .0433 inches (1.1 mm) is bent and twisted into temples, hinges, bridges, and clips. Titanium's strength and resilience ensure shape memory; far from delicate, the frames return to their original form after being subjected to daily pressure, twists, and turns. The titanium, by an electrolytical process, can be colored in a wide range of hues. Nose pads and hook ends are made of medical silicone to effectively hold the glasses in place on the face.

Sebastian Bergne (British, b. 1966) of Bergne: design for manufacture. "Lamp Shade 1" Lighting Fixture. 1992 (1991). Manufactured by Radius GmbH, Germany.

Acid-etched .006" (.015 mm) thick stainless-steel sheet, 4 3/4 x 14 3/16" (12 x 36 cm).

Sebastian Bergne's lighting fixture is based on the use of a single, minutely thin metal sheet and hardly anything else. Made from an acid-etched .006 in. (.015 cm) thick stainless-steel sheet, it shields and reflects light without hiding the functional beauty of the bulb and the fitting.

Ali Tayar (Turkish, b. 1959) of Parallel Design Partnership. "Ellen's Brackets" Shelving-System Bracket. 1993 (1993). Manufactured by Parallel Design Partnership, United States.

Extruded aluminum and stainless steel, 3 1/2 x 1 x 7 1/4" (8.9 x 2.6 x 18.4 cm).

Ali Tayar was commissioned by a friend and client to design a new bracket bookshelf system; he eventually named it "Ellen's Brackets," to honor the client. The formal inspiration came from a force-flow cantilever diagram. A uniformly loaded cantilever produces a parabolic curve starting at point zero at the tip of the cantilever, reaching its maximum at the point of support. A mounted track section and an organically shaped bracket profile are the essential elements of the design. The extrusion process permits complete freedom along two axes, while the third is determined by the direction of the extrusion. The production model consists of two custom extrusions: molten aluminum pushed through one custom die to create the "T" section for the wall-mounted track and through a second die to create the organically shaped bracket. The bracket is manufactured by slicing the aluminum extrusion into 1 in. (2.5 cm) increments. It is then drilled and cut along the back to accommodate its being slid into the wall track. Both the bracket and track are etched and anodized. The bracket is held in place by 1/4 in. (.7 cm) stainless-steel pins. The bracket's overall size was limited by the diameter of the die and by adjustments needed to translate the CNC-milled shape of the extrusion die in order to eliminate "captive" holes. The final production model of the brackets is a compromise among the often contradictory requirements of a designer's conception, the extrusion process, and streamlined machining techniques.

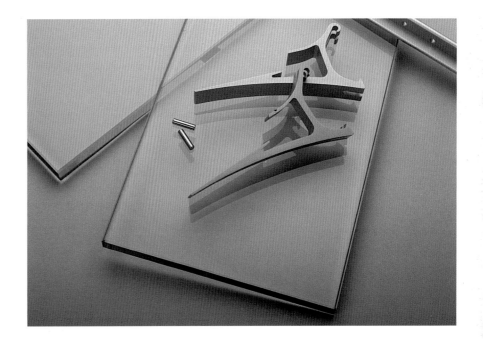

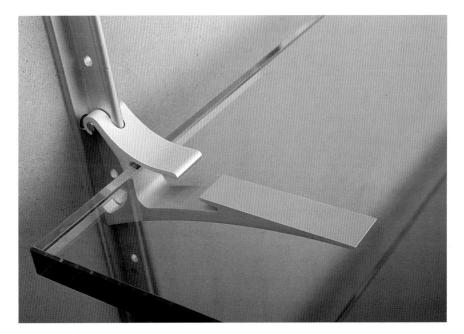

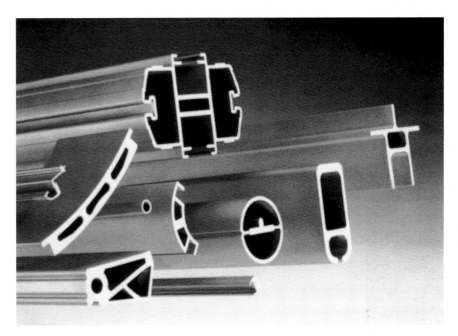

The Dow Chemical Company. Magnesium Profiles. 1987 (1987). Manufactured by Dow Chemical Co., United States.

Extruded magnesium.

Todd Wood (Canadian, b. 1969) and Allen Simpson
(Canadian, b. Great Britain 1952). "Plus-Four" Garden Tools. 1992 (1992).
Manufactured by Allen Simpson Marketing & Design, Ltd., Canada.

Recycled die-cast polished aluminum,
$10^{1}/_2$ x $2^{1}/_2$" (26.7 x 6.4 cm).

Aluminum casting is one of the most popular and expressive techniques employed in producing metal objects. In the manufacture of Todd Wood and Allen Simpson's garden tools, aluminum is melted at 1,652° F. (900° C.) and infused with silicon, copper, and iron additives for strength. It is then formed into ingots that are sent to the die-caster and melted again at the same temperature; a technician ladles the liquid aluminum into a vat fitted with an opening where the liquid is forced into a die. After this cools, the cast is opened and dual sets of garden tools are released. A press removes the surplus metal and separates the tool pairs. Imperfections on the edges are eliminated with a sanding belt. An automatic machine handles most of the polishing, but a hand-operated buffing wheel is used for final finishing of the tools.

Paolo Rizzatto (Italian, b. 1941) and Alberto Meda (Italian, b. 1945).
"Berenice" Lighting Fixture. 1985 (1984).
Manufactured by Luceplan S.p.a., Italy.

Stainless steel, aluminum, Rynite®
thermoplastic, neoprene, glass-
filled polyester, silicone rubber,
borosilicate glass, and ceramic
material; 6 dia. base x 4 dia. head x
17 3/4" each arm (15 dia. base x
10 dia. head x 45 cm each arm).

Defined both by its sleek form and the materials from which it is made, this lamp manufactured by Luceplan makes a distinctive statement about the technology of materials. The "Berenice" is constructed of forty-two components in thirteen different materials, each material corresponding to a different technology. Concerning the synergy of the lamp, Paolo Rizzatto has offered: "The lamp project is... the study of its single parts, the identification and cxperimentation with [its] respective materials and related technologies, and the composition of the various parts with each other." Since parts and materials are integral, each material is emphasized in Rizzatto's amended account: the body of the base is *die-cast aluminum* with a *lead* ballast. Die-cut *self-adhesive neoprene* was applied as a finish on the surface of the ballast. The arm is formed by two pairs of conductor rods, a tie rod, two articulated joints, and two springs. The 7/32 in. (.6 cm) diameter conductor rods are solid *drawn aluminum*. The slotted terminals are *die-cast aluminum*. The tie-rod operating the pantograph device is 5/32 in.

(.4 cm) diameter *steel*. The smaller parts include articulated joints in *injection-molded PET* (polyethylene terephthalate, also known as Rynite by Du Pont), a bulb holder in a *ceramic* material, a miniaturized on/off switch in *steel* coated with *silicone rubber*, a parabolic reflector in *glass*, a filter with a *stainless-steel* ring and flat ultraviolet-filtering *borosilicate glass*, and the knurled ring for moving the reflector in *pressed glass*.

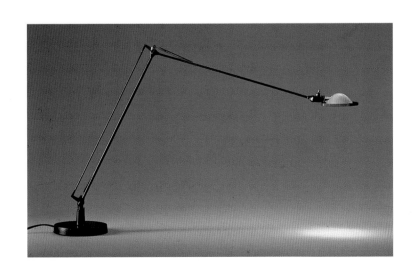

Water Studio Co. "O-Product" Camera. 1988 (1987). Manufactured by Olympus Optical Co., Ltd., Japan. Aluminum, steel, and other materials; 3 7/8 x 3 1/8 x 1 13/16" (9.9 x 8.2 x 4.5 cm) body, 3 x 1 15/16 x 1 13/16" (7.5 x 4.8 x 4.5 cm) flash.

The "O-Product" camera was designed as a limited-edition collector's model, issued in 1989 to celebrate Olympus Optical's seventieth anniversary and the sesquicentennial of the invention of photography. Easy-to-form aluminum, with its vast range of other applications, was chosen for the molded shell, whose unexpected shape masks a conventional, though technologically advanced, apparatus: the 35mm-lens shutter camera. Large eyes pierce the face of a cylindrical form that emerges from a soft-cornered rectangular box; standard screw heads are incongruous partners in a mixture of contemporary and traditional aesthetics.

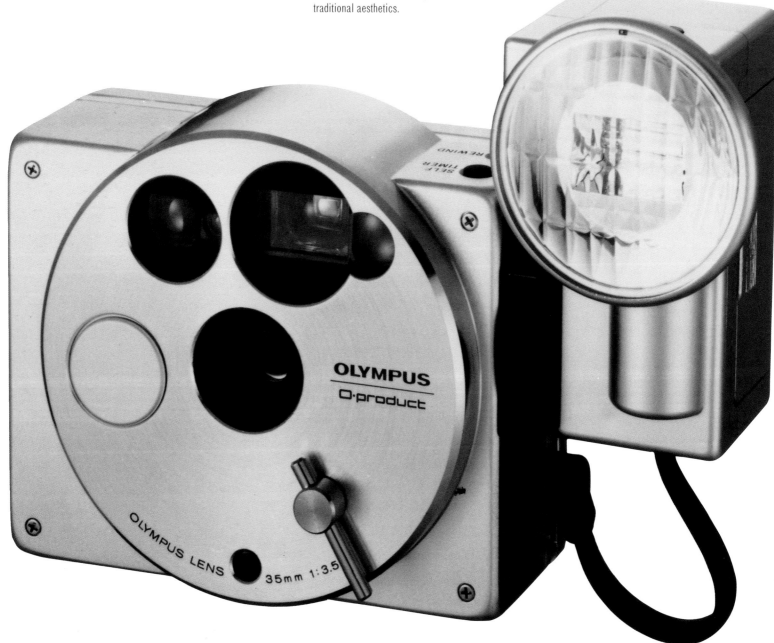

Jay Wilson (American, b. 1941) and Ted Bryant (American, b. 1959) of GVO. "ThetaScan" Autocollimator (Laser Measuring Instrument). (1992). Prototype. Stainless steel and RPM (rubber plaster mold) aluminum, 4 x 9 x 14" (10.2 x 22.7 x 35.6 cm).

An autocollimator is a highly precise instrument capable of measuring angles at distant points as far away as 10 miles (15.4 km) in increments equivalent to the thickness of a human hair. The "ThetaScan" is mechanically focused on three different axis points. Through the eyepiece of the scope, the finely tuned laser-beam dot focuses on a mirror in the distance. After the target is aligned, the laser beam reflected by the mirror is cast back through the lens to a receptor that calculates the angle of incidence. The machined barrel assembly is made of stainless steel and passivated (a process that protects against contamination by a coating or surface treatment, in this case a radial finish). The cast-aluminum base, produced with selective secondary machining, is finished with a fused powder coating. The RPM molding process makes the cast aluminum durable and is capable of creating complex forms with undercuts, thus reducing the number of parts required. All the components of the autocollimator are mounted to the barrel, a single piece of machined stainless steel.

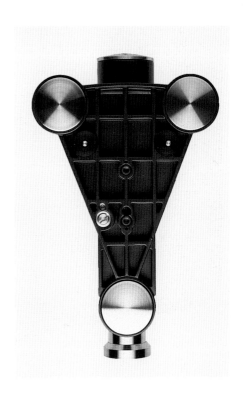

For their strength, metals of all kinds have been used for centuries as the primary material for the manufacture of vehicles. Only recently has their preeminence been threatened by nonmetallic composites, more often for outer shells. Strongly suggesting modernity, the machine aesthetic, and a newborn vigor between the world wars, bent tubular steel became the canonical symbol of the modern movement, particularly for furniture. Yet the wheelchair and HPV here offer two contemporary tubular-metal applications.

Kazuo Kawasaki (Japanese, b. 1949). "Carna" Folding Wheelchair. 1991 (1989). Manufactured by SIG Workshop Co., Ltd., Japan.

Titanium frame, rubber seat and tires, and aluminum honeycomb-core disk wheels; 33 x 22 x 35 1/4" (84 x 56 x 89.6 cm). The Museum of Modern Art, New York, gift of the designer.

The light, stylish "Carna" folding wheelchair weighs only 13 lbs. (5.9 kg). It features a titanium frame for lightness, oversized wheels similar to those on racing chairs for stability, and a separate foldaway seat-and-back unit for portability. The seat and back are fitted with either urethane or air-inflated mats. The disk wheels are built of aluminum with a honeycomb core and the push-rims of 1 in. (2.6 cm) titanium pipe.

Michael Burrows (British, b. 1943) of Burrows Engineering. "Windcheetah T.I." HPV (Human-Powered Vehicle). 1995 (1992). Manufactured by The Seat of the Pants Co., Ltd., Great Britain.

Titanium, aluminum, carbon Kevlar®, and hand-cast lugs bonded to aluminum tubes; 32 5/8 x 28 1/8 x 78 3/4" (88 x 71.5 x 200 cm).

More than a decade has passed since the original model of the "Windcheetah" was invented by Michael Burrows. Only 160 examples have been produced since its introduction. Bob Dixon recently acquired the rights for production by his firm, The Seat of the Pants. The peculiar-looking self-propelled machine is an amalgamation of high-tech materials, handcrafted and designed to amplify human muscle power. A high-quality aluminum alloy known as LM25, more easily machined than conventional alloys, is used for the hand-cast lugs. The reinforced plastic seat on Burrows's original model was made of carbon Kevlar; the upholstered version here incorporates athletic-shoe foam. The steering, brakes, and 24-speed gear shift are located at the end of a single control stick. The 6063-specification-alloy tubular frame is manufactured in three sizes, and, when fully assembled, the "Windcheetah" weighs 35 lbs. (16 kg). The custom-made "T.I." model uses titanium in the spokes, rear hubs, stub axles, king-pin assemblies, and bottom brackets.

Hisanori Masuda (Japanese, b. 1949). "Iquom" Tableware Collection.
C. 1989 (c. 1989). Manufactured by Kikuchi Hojudo, Inc., Japan.

Recycled sand-cast aluminium, dimensions vary.

Exposed to the rich centuries-old tradition of the metal crafts in Japan's Yamagata Prefecture where he lives and works, Hisanori Masuda realized the possibilities that only aluminum can offer in making the kind of refined objects for which he has become known. A pioneer in recycling experimentation, Masuda has manipulated a mutant material possibly to its zenith. For his tableware, he achieves the appearance of quicksilver by sand-casting reprocessed aluminum.

Acknowledgments

The planning of *Mutant Materials in Contemporary Design* began in July 1994, and both the exhibition and publication necessarily kept to a fast-paced schedule. A complicated undertaking such as this owes its success to the crucial support of many colleagues and friends. A large number of designers, company executives, and associates at The Museum of Modern Art have gone out of their way to help me bring this exhibition to fruition, and I owe them all many thanks for their generosity of time and effort.

On behalf of The Museum of Modern Art, I thank the numerous companies and individuals who made generous commitments to the various parts of the exhibition and catalogue and patiently responded to all of my requests for technical data. In particular, I would like to thank Gaetano Pesce for conceiving and realizing a brilliant resin cover for a special edition of the catalogue. His contribution, which involved a great deal of time and experimentation, has highlighted the meaning of the exhibition and transformed each of these books into a unique object. The polyurethane resin for the cover was kindly donated by Ciba-Geigy Corporation, and I would like to express my profound gratitude to Thomas E. Preiswerk, of Ciba Communications in Basel; David G. Taylor, Vice President, Public Affairs and Communication, and Lois S. Amend, Director, External Affairs Program, of Ciba's Ardsley, New York, headquarters; and Bill Geresy, Product Manager, Ciba Formulated Materials Group. Rolf Fehlbaum, Director of Vitra International and a member of the Museum's Architecture and Design Committee, supported the project and facilitated our contact with Ciba. I am especially grateful to him.

In the research phase, I was assisted by friends who sent ideas and objects for consideration from all over the world, and who gave precious advice and assistance. I would like to thank them one by one, but it would take too many pages to name them all; I must, however, single out a few. Kayoko Ota, Editor of *Telescope* magazine, shared with me her network of acquaintances. David Kusuma, of Miles Polymers Design Group, introduced me to the Industrial Designers' Society of America's Materials and Processes Interest Group. Samuel B. Frank, former Director of Architecture and Design, and Lezli H. White, Supervisor of Marketing Communications for the Advanced Materials and Process Technologies Division, Corning Incorporated, explained to me the mysterious world of glass. Jean Mayer, Research Microbiologist at the Biotechnology Division of the U.S. Army in Natick, Massachusetts, was very helpful and gave us crucial contacts on alternative materials.

I am also grateful to Takatoshi Ide, Takenobu Igarashi, Tetsuro Itoh, Tadanori Nagasawa, Yasuko Seki, and Noriko Takiguchi from Japan; Ulf Mannervik from Sweden; Chantal Hamaïde from France; David Redhead and Daniel Weil from Great Britain; Verena Turrian-Keller from Switzerland; Tibor Kalman, Frida Doveil, and the wonderful staffs of the magazines *Abitare* and *Domus*, who also provided many photographic materials for the catalogue, from Italy; and George Beylerian, Tim Brown, David Schwartz, Julie Taylor, and many others in the United States. Ivan Luini, Judith Nasatir, and Chee Pearlman, good friends and articulate critics, along with friends and fellow architects Milena Brambilla and Giuseppe Barillari, patiently brainstormed with me on the various aspects of the project.

A number of experts in the design of materials and their applications allowed me to interview them and gave me useful information and insights for my essay. Thus, for their patience and time I wish to thank James Carpenter (glass), Guy Nordenson (metals), Stephen Peart (rubber and foam), Gaetano Pesce (plastics), Burt Rutan (fibers and composites), Kari Virtanen (wood), and Eva Zeisel (ceramics).

For essential outside help on the installation of the exhibition, I am grateful to Donald Francis and Scott Keon of the Intrepid Air and Space Museum in New York, who advised us on the hanging of the carbon-fiber airplane at the entrance of the show. The glass text panels are the work and gift of Claudio Cesar.

I especially would like to thank the entire staff of The Museum of Modern Art for its enthusiastic support of this endeavor. In particular, I thank Agnes Gund, Chairman of the Board, whose early and unwavering support was crucial to the realization of the exhibition;

Richard E. Oldenburg, Director Emeritus, under whose stewardship the project was initiated; and Glenn D. Lowry, Director Designate, under whose aegis this project has seen the light. James S. Snyder, Deputy Director for Planning and Program Support, and Kirk Varnedoe, Chief Curator, Department of Painting and Sculpture, graciously permitted the special installation of the airplane in the Garden Hall; Mr. Varnedoe was especially cooperative in helping to redefine the exhibition space. I also thank the Exhibitions Committee for believing in the exhibition; the Contemporary Arts Council for their solid support; Richard Palmer, Coordinator of Exhibitions, for patiently working out the complicated administrative details attached to such a short-term project; Diane Farynyk, Registrar, and Ramona Bronkar Bannayan, Associate Registrar, for keeping track of so many diverse loan items, scattered in dimensions and time; Jessica Schwartz, Director of Public Information, and Mary-Lou Strahllendorf, Press Representative, for their publicity efforts; Daniel Vecchitto, Director of Development, John L. Wielk, Manager, Exhibition and Project Funding, Robert I. Smith, Jr., Manager, Corporate Relations, for their efforts in securing funding for the show; and Ralph Destino, Chairman of the Business Committee, for his kind support. I also wish to thank Stephen Clark, Assistant General Counsel, for his invaluable advice, and my colleagues Barbara London and Sheryl Conkelton for their input.

A special acknowledgment goes to the Department of Publications, directed by Osa Brown, and to the Department of Exhibition Production and Design, directed by Jerome Neuner. Both departments were involved in an unusually fast and complex project, and both directors were enthusiastic and open to unusual ideas. In Publications I would particularly like to thank Harriet Schoenholz Bee, Managing Editor, for her guidance and for her supervision of the editorial process, and Marc Sapir, Assistant Production Manager, who solved many of the technical problems attached to the resin cover and kept everyone on schedule. My thanks also go to my good friend Mel Byars, who edited the catalogue texts; to Barbara Ross Geiger, who completed them; and to Sherri Fuchs, Managing Editor of *Plastics Technology* magazine, who kindly reviewed the technical terms used in the plates section. Jody Hanson, Director of Graphics, supervised the production of the catalogue, which was designed by Eric Baker, who deserves my gratitude for his work. Last but not least, Greg Van Alstyne, Senior Graphic Designer, was responsible for the graphics used throughout the installation.

In the Department of Architecture and Design, I wish to thank Terence Riley, Chief Curator, who was the first to believe strongly in this exhibition and who has offered his support throughout the project. I would also like to acknowledge Peter Reed, Associate Curator, for his intelligent comments about the catalogue essay, and Matilda McQuaid, Assistant Curator, for her generous advice on many aspects of the exhibition. Yanitza Tavarez, Curatorial Intern, was my tireless and indispensable assistant in this project, an inventive problem-solver, and a valuable interlocutor. Hideki Yamamoto, Curatorial Intern, enabled me to gain access to information and corporations that the language barrier would otherwise have kept obscure and enthusiastically did the initial research. The department was remarkably supportive and helpful, and I thank each of its members.

The idea for *Mutant Materials* evolved from earlier exhibitions that I organized and from a series of articles that I wrote. For support in this extensive period of research and for much more, I am indebted to Achille Castiglioni, Pierluigi Cerri, Italo Lupi, Vittorio Magnago Lampugnani, and Paolo Viti. Two other sources of inspiration need to be mentioned. The first is a book by Ezio Manzini, *La Materia dell'invenzione.* The second is Maya, a beautiful mutant in *Space 1999*, a science-fiction television series of the mid-1970s. As an effective representation of the positive aspects of mutancy, however fictional, she provided the suggestion of the title of the show.

This book is dedicated to Giulio Castelli, a pioneer in the study and application of mutant materials, founder of the Kartell company, and my friend and mentor.

—P. A.

Lenders to the Exhibition

Advanced Elastomer Systems L.P., St. Louis
Alias S.r.l., Grumello del Monte, Italy
Harry Allen, New York
Asahi Glass Co., Ltd, Tokyo
Authentics-Artipresent GmbH, Holzgerlingen, Germany
Avocet, Inc., Palo Alto
Bausch & Lomb, Inc., Rochester, N.Y.
Bell Sports, Inc., Los Gatos, Calif.
Sebastian Bergne, London
Biedermann Motech GmbH, Schweningen, Germany
Bio Mechanical Composites, Camarillo, Calif.
Boone Technologies, Kennesaw, Ga.
Constantin Boym, New York
Callaway Golf Co., Carlsbad, Calif.
James Carpenter, New York
Donald Carr, Dayton, Ohio
Claudio Cesar, Burlington, Calif.
Chevron Chemical Co., Orange, Tex.
The Christian Brothers, Inc., Warroad, Minn.
The Christy Company, Pleasanton, Calif.
Consortium Replastic, Rome
Dainese S.p.a., Molvena, Italy
Danese S.r.l., Grumello del Monte, Italy
Design Continuum, Inc., Boston
Details, New York
Domus Academy, Milan
Dow Chemical Co., Midland, Mich.
Du Pont Polymer Products, Wilmington, Del.
Dynamic Systems, Inc., Leicester, N.C.
Renate Eilert, Vallans, France
EnviroSafe Products, Inc., New York
Bob Evans Designs, Inc., Santa Barbara
Fenwick, Inc., Huntington Beach, Calif.
Figla Co., Ltd., Tokyo
Flos S.p.a., Brescia, Italy
frogdesign, Sunnyvale, Calif.
GVO, Inc., Palo Alto
Go Video, Inc., Scottsdale, Ariz.
Eric Goetz Custom Sailboats, Inc., Bristol, R.I.
Goetz Marine Technology (GMT), Inc., Bristol, R.I.
Donald Goodall, Blakehurst, Australia
Hikari Products, Inc., Gardena, Calif.
IBM Corporation, Armonk, N.Y.
IDEO Product Development, Palo Alto
IDEO Product Development, San Francisco
Takeshi Ishiguro, Tokyo
Kaiser Aluminum Co., Pleasanton, Calif.
Kartell S.p.a., Milan
Kazuo Kawasaki, Fukui, Japan
The Kemper Museum of Contemporary Art and Design
          of Kansas City Art Institute, Kansas City, Mo.
Kikuchi Hojudo, Inc., Yamagata, Japan
The Knoll Group, New York
Krohn/Abbott Unlimited, Los Angeles
Masayuki Kurokawa, Tokyo
Kyocera International, Inc., San Diego
Lancair International, Inc., Redmond, Ore.
Lindberg Optic Design, Aabyhøj, Denmark
Stefan Lindfors, Kansas City, Mo.
Logitech, Inc., Fremont, Calif.
Aaron Lown, New York
Luceplan USA, New York
MAP (Merchants of Australian Products Pty., Ltd.), Melbourne
Maderón Promotion Agency, Barcelona
Magis S.r.l., Motta Livenza, Italy
Vincent Marino, Olympus America, Inc., Woodbury, N.Y.
Martin Archery, Walla Walla, Wash.
Maunsell Structural Plastics, Ltd., Kent, Great Britain
Mazda Motor Corporation, Irvine, Calif.
Metrokane, Inc., New York
Moroso S.p.a., Cavalicco, Italy

Nambe Mills, Inc., Santa Fe, N.M.
Neico Aviation, Inc., Redmond, Ore.
Nemo S.r.l., Rovellasca, Italy
Neste Oy, Espoo, Finland
Nike, Inc., Beaverton, Ore.
Ninaber/Peters/Krouwel Industrial Design, Leiden
Nixalite of America, Inc., East Moline, Ill.
Okamura Corporation, Tokyo
Pentagram Design, Ltd., London
Perception, Inc., Easley, S.C.
Gordon Randall Perry, New York
Plantronics, Inc., Santa Cruz, Calif.
RADO Watch Co., Ltd., Switzerland
Karim England Rashid, New York
Sanford Redmond, New York
Rollerblade, Inc., Minnetonka, Minn.
Royal College of Art, London
Santa Cruz Snowboards (NHS/Inc.), Santa Cruz, Calif.
Schott Process Systems, Inc., Vineland, N.J.
The Seat of the Pants Co., Ltd., Cheshire, Great Britain
Seiko Epson Corporation, Nagano, Japan
Sharp Electronics Corporation, Mahwah, N.J.
Allen Simpson, Ontario
Peter Stathis, Cold Spring, N.Y.
Sỳn S.r.l., Milan
Syndesis, Inc., Santa Monica
Ali Tayar, New York
The Thermos Co., Shamburg, Ill.
Thomson Consumer Electronics, Courbevole, France
3M Unitek, Monrovia, Calif.
Unifor, Inc., New York
Vent Design, Campbell, Calif.
Viracon, Owatonna, Minn.
Steve Visser, West Lafayette, Ind.
WRS Group, Inc., Waco, Tex.
Willat Writing Instruments, Los Angeles
Carl Zeiss Ferngläser, Aalen, Germany
Zelco Industries, Inc., Mt. Vernon, N.Y.

Courtesy Advanced Elastomer Systems, L.P., St. Louis: 80 top
Alexander, Glass, Ingersol, Inc., courtesy Donald Carr, Dayton, Ohio: 32 top
Paola Antonelli, New York: 53, 101 bottom left and right
Courtesy Ron Arad Associates, London: 16 top
Courtesy Avocet, Inc., Palo Alto: 70 bottom
BWJ (Renzo Piano Building Workshop Japan), Osaka: 76 bottom, 77
Aldo Ballo, Milan, courtesy Danese S.r.l., Milan: 20, 96
Aldo Ballo, Milan, courtesy Samuel Lucente, IBM Corporation, Armonk, N.Y.: 64 top, 64 bottom
Courtesy Bausch & Lomb, Inc., Rochester, N.Y.: 23 top
Courtesy Sebastian Bergne, London: 112 top, 114
Bernini S.p.a., Carate Brianza, Italy, courtesy Gaetano Pesce, New York: 27
Tom Bonnard, courtesy David Hertz, Santa Monica: 41 top
Sally Andersen Bruce, New Milford, Conn., courtesy Samuel Lucente, IBM Corporation, Armonk, N.Y.: 64 center
Courtesy CSAC, Parma, Italy: 16 bottom
Courtesy Callaway Golf, Carlsbad, Calif.: 110 top left and right
Courtesy James Carpenter, New York: 88, 94, 95 bottom left and right
Courtesy Giulio Castelli, Milan: 14 top
Donald Chadwick, Santa Monica: 56 top
Courtesy The Christian Brothers, Inc., Warroad, Minn.: 107 bottom left, center, and right
Mario Ciampi, courtesy Ceccotti S.p.a., Pisa: 17
Courtesy Ciba Heath Tecna Aerospace Co., Kent, Wash.: 15
Walter Civardi, New York: 44
Courtesy Corning Incorporated, Corning, N.Y.: 12 right
Tony Curatolla, courtesy Metrokane, Inc., New York: 22
Liz Deschenes, New York, courtesy Harry Allen, New York: 48 bottom, 49 bottom right
Courtesy Design Continuum, Inc., Boston: 71
Donato Di Bello, courtesy Domus Archives, Milan: 104, 105
Donato Di Bello, courtesy Sỳn S.r.l., Milan: 112 bottom
Courtesy Domus Academy, Milan: 40 top
Courtesy Dow Chemical Co., Midland, Mich.: 115 bottom
Rick English, San Francisco, courtesy Logitech, Inc., Fremont, Calif.: 33 bottom
Bob Evans, Santa Barbara: 23 bottom
Courtesy FM Design, West Midlands, Great Britain: 110 bottom
Courtesy Figla Co., Ltd., Tokyo: 90, 91
Courtesy Flos S.p.a., Brescia, Italy: 79 bottom, 92 top left and right, left, bottom right
Courtesy frogdesign, Sunnyvale, Calif.: 58 top, 80 bottom left
Mitsumasa Fujitsuka, Tokyo, courtesy Kazuo Kawasaki, Fukui, Japan:120
Courtesy GVO, Inc., Palo Alto: 80 bottom right
Doug Hall, Toronto, courtesy Karim England Rashid, New York: 88 bottom
Dietmar Henneka, Stuttgart, courtesy Logitech, Inc., Fremont, Calif.: 32 bottom
Courtesy Takeshi Ishiguro, Tokyo: 54
Michael Jones, courtesy Ziba Design, Huntington Beach, Calif.: 36 top
Courtesy Kaiser Aluminum Co., Pleasanton, Calif.: 109
Courtesy Kartell S.p.a., Milan: 12 left, 29 bottom, 40 bottom
Kate Keller, The Museum of Modern Art, New York: 11, 14 bottom, 31 bottom, 40 center, 55 bottom, 58 bottom, 59, 72 bottom, 73 bottom, 78 bottom, 93 bottom, 106 top, 107 top
Charles Kemper, San Francisco, courtesy IDEO Product Development, Palo Alto: 37
Kelley King, Santa Ana, Calif., courtesy GVO, Inc., Palo Alto: 119
Courtesy The Knoll Group, New York: 78 top
Lisa Krohn, Los Angeles: 99
Courtesy Masayuki Kurokawa, Tokyo: 39, 85
Courtesy Kyocera International, Inc., San Diego: 10, 46, 47 bottom
Courtesy Lindberg Optic Design, Aabyhøj, Denmark: 113
Courtesy Ross Lovegrove, London: 30, 51
Aaron Lown, New York: 50 left, 67 bottom
Courtesy Maderón Promotion Agency, Barcelona: 102, 103
Courtesy Hisanori Masuda, Yamagata, Japan: 122, 123, and cover
Courtesy Maunsell Structural Plastics, Ltd., Kent, Great Britain: 66
Courtesy Alberto Meda, Milan: 62 top, 62 bottom, 63 right top and bottom
Trevor Mein, courtesy MAP International, Melbourne: 42, 75
Marco Melander, courtesy Stefan Lindfors, Kansas City, Mo.: 38 top
Steven Michael: 18

Courtesy Herman Miller, Inc., Zeeland, Mich.: 56 bottom, 57
Courtesy The Museum of Modern Art, New York: 8
Stan Musliek, San Francisco, courtesy IDEO Product Development, Palo Alto: 33 top
Courtesy Neico Aviation, Inc., Redmond, Ore.: 60 right, 61
Courtesy Nike, Inc., Beaverton, Ore.: 72 top, 73 top
Courtesy Ninaber/Peters/Krouwel Industrial Design, Leiden: 31 top
Okamura Corporation, Tokyo: 76 top
Courtesy Olympus America, Inc., Woodbury, N.Y.: 118
Douglas M. Parker Studio, Los Angeles, courtesy Margo Leavin Gallery, Los Angeles: 19
Courtesy Pentagram Design, Ltd., London: 26
Courtesy Perception, Inc., Easley, S.C.: 60 left
Parrish Puente, courtesy Gaetano Pesce, New York: 43
Courtesy Quantum Chemical Co., Cincinnati: 97
Courtesy RADO Watch Co., Ltd., Lengnau, Switzerland: 45, 50 right
Courtesy Sanford Redmond, New York: 38 bottom
Courtesy Riedell Skating Shoes, Inc., Red Wing, Minn.: 58 center
Courtesy Paolo Rizzatto, Milan: 117
Courtesy Rollerblade, Inc., Minnetonka, Minn.: 36 bottom
Courtesy Burt Rutan, Mojave, Calif.: 52
Benvenuto Saba, courtesy Abitare, Milan: 28 top left
Courtesy Marc Sadler, Asolo, Italy: 79 top, 84
E.G. Schempf, courtesy Stefan Lindfors, Kansas City, Mo.: 67 top
Courtesy Schott Process Systems, Inc., Vineland, N.J.: 89
Courtesy The Seat of the Pants Co., Ltd., Cheshire, Great Britain: 121
Mikio Sekita, courtesy James Carpenter, New York: 95 top
Courtesy Selee Corporation, Hendersonville, N.C.: 48 top left and right
Roberto Sellitto, Milan, courtesy Alberto Meda, Milan: 62 bottom left, 63 left
Roberto Sellitto, Milan, courtesy Nemo S.r.l., Rovellasca, Italy: 98
Courtesy Silvana Sermisoni, Milan: 74
Courtesy Sharp Corporation, Osaka: 9
Allen Simpson, Ontario: 116
Smith & Hawkins, courtesy David Hertz, Santa Monica: 41 bottom right
Brian Stanton, Croton-on-Hudson, N.Y., courtesy Mazda Motor Corporation, Irvine, Calif.: 24, 25
Peter Stathis, Cold Spring, N.Y.: 81 bottom right
Courtesy Steelcase, Inc., Grand Rapids, Mich.: 13, 89
Steelcase, Inc., Grand Rapids, Mich., courtesy David Hertz, Santa Monica: 41 bottom left
Courtesy Sỳn S.r.l., Milan: 34 top
Courtesy Ali Tayar, New York: 115 top
Courtesy The Thermos Co., Shamburg, Ill.: 111
Courtesy 3M Unitek, Monrovia, Calif.: 47 top
Leo Torri, courtesy Abitare, Milan: 28 top right, bottom
Courtesy Shozo Toyohisa, Kanagawa, Japan: 55 top
Courtesy Vent Design, Campbell, Calif.: 33 center left and right
Vent Design, Campbell, Calif., courtesy Domus Archives, Milan: 69, 83
Courtesy Steve Visser, West Lafayette, Ind.: 35
Courtesy WRS Group, Inc., Waco, Tex.: 70 top left and right
Bill Waltzer, courtesy Gordon Randall Perry, New York: 34 bottom
Paul Warchol, New York: 108
Joshua White, courtesy Frank O. Gehry Associates, Santa Monica: 96, 100
Kenneth Willardt, courtesy Smart Design, New York: 81 top, 81 bottom left
Miro Zagnoli, courtesy Domus Archives, Milan: 29 top
Courtesy Zelco Industries, Inc., Mt. Vernon, N.Y.: 93 top